Historical Manuscript Depositories in Pennsylvania

COMPILED BY

IRWIN RICHMAN

COMMONWEALTH OF PENNSYLVANIA

THE PENNSYLVANIA HISTORICAL AND
MUSEUM COMMISSION

Harrisburg, 1965

THE PENNSYLVANIA HISTORICAL AND MUSEUM COMMISSION

JAMES B. STEVENSON, *Chairman*

HERMAN BLUM

EDWIN B. CODDINGTON

RALPH HAZELTINE

MRS. FERNE SMITH HETRICK

MRS. HENRY P. HOFFSTOT, JR.

MAURICE A. MOOK

CHARLES G. WEBB

THOMAS ELLIOTT WYNNE

GEORGE W. HOFFMAN, *ex officio*
Acting Superintendent of Public Instruction

MEMBERS FROM THE GENERAL ASSEMBLY

JAMES KEPLER DAVIS, *Representative*   J. DEAN POLEN, *Representative*

PAUL W. MAHADY, *Senator*   JOHN H. WARE, III, *Senator*

TRUSTEES EX OFFICIO

WILLIAM W. SCRANTON, *Governor of the Commonwealth*

GRACE M. SLOAN, *Auditor General*

THOMAS Z. MINEHART, *State Treasurer*

ADMINISTRATIVE STAFF

SYLVESTER K. STEVENS, *Executive Director*

WILLIAM J. WEWER, *Executive Assistant*

WILLIAM N. RICHARDS, *Director*
Bureau of Museums, Historic Sites, and Properties

DONALD H. KENT, *Director*
Bureau of Research, Publications, and Records

Foreword

Like the *Bibliography of Pennsylvania History,* published by the Pennsylvania Historical and Museum Commission in 1957, the present guide to manuscript depositories is expected to be especially useful to students of Pennsylvania history, both State and local; however, manuscripts relating to American history more generally are also included. In contrast to Philip M. Hamer's more inclusive *Guide to the Archives and Manuscripts in the United States* (New Haven: Yale University Press, 1961), the present work is limited not only to Pennsylvania institutions but also to manuscripts relating to American history. Public records (municipal, county, or State) are not included, nor are an organization's own institutional records.

Ranging less widely, the present survey in a sense covers more ground: Working in a smaller geographical area, the compiler himself has been able to visit almost all the institutions reported, rather than having to depend upon mailed questionnaires, and so has been able to include more depositories than otherwise would have been possible. Despite the narrower definition of field, the present work's 105 entries include twenty-seven that do not appear in the Pennsylvania section of the larger United States *Guide.*

All entries in the present work are based on visits to the respective institutions or, in a few instances, on detailed correspondence with them; and the entries were subsequently submitted to these institutions for possible correction and final approval. If, despite this care, any significant manuscript holdings have been missed, the Pennsylvania Historical and Museum Commission would be grateful for information to be included in a later edition.

For the completion of his work, the compiler is especially indebted to the staffs of all the institutions herein listed. Thanks are due the members of the Historical and Museum Commission and to the Executive Director, Dr. S. K. Stevens, who authorized the survey and approved the publication. Mr. Donald H. Kent, Director of the Bureau of Research, Publications, and Records, and Mr. William A. Hunter, Chief of the Division of Research and Publications, provided editorial direction; Mr. Harold L. Meyers, Associate Historian, oversaw the arrangements for printing; and Miss Dorothy Bruszo, Miss Patricia Lesko, Miss Carol Thomas, and Mrs. Elsa B. Hughes did the indispensable work of typing the various revisions of the manuscript. Mrs. Gail Gibson, Assistant Historian, prepared the index.

Historical Manuscript
Depositories in Pennsylvania

Allentown

LEHIGH COUNTY HISTORICAL SOCIETY

Trout Hall, Allentown.

Secretary: William G. Genszler

Hours: 10:00 A. M.-12:00 M., 1:00-4:00 P. M., Tuesday through Friday. Address correspondence to Mr. Genzler at 752 North 19th Street, Allentown.

HOLDINGS: Approximately 4 cubic feet of manuscript materials, largely arranged and catalogued. Included are *William J. Reichard Letters* (1862-1863), 140 letters written to his family by a soldier who served in both the 128th and the 41st Regts. of Pa. Volun.; *Church Records* of 7 Lehigh County churches; and a letter book of Jacob Weiss (1778-1781), a deputy quartermaster general who served at Valley Forge; and others.

COPY SERVICES: Photocopying can be arranged.

SEE: *Proceedings of the Lehigh County Historical Society,* XXI (1956) and XXII (1958).

Altoona

BLAIR COUNTY HISTORICAL SOCIETY

Baker Mansion, Altoona.

Curator: J. J. Hauser

Hours: By appointment, June through October. Address correspondence to Mr. Jesse L. Hartman, President, Hollidaysburg.

HOLDINGS: Approximately 6 cubic feet of manuscript materials, both arranged and catalogued. Included are *Allegheny Furnace Records* (1840-1875); *Allegheny Portage Railroad Books and Papers* (1834-1857), ca. 1,000 items which not only deal directly with the railroad's operation (esp. during the superintendencies of John Snodgrass [1839-1843] and William S. Campbell [1850-1851], but also with business of the area's merchants and hotel keepers whose livelihood was dependent on the railroad; *Higgins Collection* (1815-c.1865), ca. 1,300 items consisting of ca. 300 incoming letters (1815-1850) addressed to Joseph

1

Higgins, which are concerned with the Portage Iron Works at Duncansville, which he managed—most of the letters discuss the problems of iron making and nail manufacturing—and ca. 1,000 items relating to the Mexican and Civil War careers of Col. Jacob Higgins; and others.

COPY SERVICES: None.

SEE: Hubertis M. Cummings, comp., *Pennsylvania Board of Canal Commissioners' Records with Allied Records of Canal Companies Chartered by the Commonwealth, Descriptive Index*, Harrisburg: Commonwealth of Pennsylvania, Department of Internal Affairs, 1959, pp. 233-235.

Ambridge

OLD ECONOMY VILLAGE

Pennsylvania Historical and Museum Commission, Ambridge.

Curator: Dr. Lawrence Thurman

Hours: 8:30 A. M.-5:00 P. M. daily.

HOLDINGS: Approximately 363 cubic feet of materials consisting of some 500,000 items, including *Correspondence Collection* (1790-1951), ca. 200 cubic feet of business, personal, and religious letters to and from the leaders of the society from George Rapp to John Duss, business receipts, and legal documents; *Ledger Collection* (1805-1926), ca. 120 cubic feet, consisting of 1,084 volumes which show all economic transactions of the society; *Music Collection* (1805-1905), ca. 40 cubic feet of music written by members of the Harmony Society; and ca. 1 cubic foot of genealogical material in the form of index cards compiled concerning 1,113 members of the society; and others.

COPY SERVICES: Photocopies and microfilm available through the Commission.

Annville

LEBANON VALLEY COLLEGE

College Library, Annville.

Librarian: Donald E. Fields

Hours: Academic year: 8:00 A. M.-5:00 P. M., Monday through Friday; 9:00 A. M.-12:00 M., 1:00-3:00 P. M., Saturday; 2:00-5:00 P. M., Sunday. Summer: 8:00 A. M.-4:00 P. M., Monday through Friday.

HOLDINGS: Approximately 8 cubic feet of manuscript materials, arranged and catalogued. Included are *School Records Collection* (1822-1897), record books kept by schools in Millcreek district (1884-1885), Mount Joy (1822-1823), North Annville district (1871-1877, 1890-1897), and Conewago district (1861-1865), also 4 school exercise books (1824-1847); *Commercial Records Collection* (1768-1900), 61 ledgers and daybooks of business enterprises in Lebanon, Berks, and Dauphin counties, Pennsylvania, and Sussex County, New Jersey—the largest grouping in this collection is the 53 volumes relating to the Henry Shavely Heilman grain mill in Lebanon; interesting miscellanea include the daybooks of three generations of local 19th C. physicians, John Tryor, John Michael, and Louis A. Livingood; civil dockets kept by John Felix Light, justice of the peace of North Annville (1873-1886, 1893-1904) ; a few letters from the family of Lloyd Mifflin (1783-1836) ; and others.

COPY SERVICES: Limited photocopying available.

Athens

TIOGA POINT MUSEUM

724 S. Main St., Athens.

Director: Mrs. Lyle Jackson

Hours: 7:00-9:00 P. M., Monday; 2:00-5:00 P. M., Wednesday and Saturday. It is wise, however, to make an appointment.

HOLDINGS: Approximately 16.75 cubic feet of manuscripts only partially arranged and catalogued. Included are *Chemung and Junction Canals and Railroads Papers* (1843-1873) , ca. .50 cubic foot of business correspondence and minutes of the operation in which George M. Hollenback and C. F. Welles, Jr., had an interest; *Reverand David Craft Collection,* ca. 15 cubic feet of materials collected for his 1878 history of Bradford County, which includes not only notes, but a large number of original documents, including John Franklin items, letters to and from Joseph Kingsberry, and letters from Gouverneur Morris; *Col. John Franklin Collection* (1817-1831) , ca. .06 cubic foot including letters, his will, his pardon, and his account book (1822-1831) ; *Hollenback Papers* (1791-1843) , ca. .75 cubic foot of business correspondence relating to the Hollenback trading posts in Tioga, Wilkes-Barre, Wyoming, and Wysox—there are many letters from Stephen Tuttle, Jr., to Matthias Hollenback, Mrs. Sarah Hollenback, and Henry Welles; *Louise Welles and Elsie Murray Collection,* ca. .40 cubic foot of materials pertaining to Azilum, including a letter book of John Keating (1818-1820) , an account book of Hollenback's store at Tioga Point (1793) , which sold to Azilum, kept by a clerk, Guy Maxwell, several contemporary letters, etc.; *Tidd Autograph Collection,* ca. .01 cubic foot—although small, this collection has several important items, including a letter of George Washington dated at Valley Forge, December 29, 1777, to Governor Cooke of Rhode Island, and a letter from John Adams to Richard Cranch (1783) discussing the Treaty of Paris—other documents of interest are items of John Hancock, Abraham Lincoln, William Penn, and Benjamin Franklin; interesting miscellaneous items in the museum's collections include the Athens Township road tax book (1829-1842) and two letters (1822) written by Lafayette to F. J. Pesse; and others.

COPY SERVICES: None.

Bethlehem

ARCHIVES OF THE MORAVIAN CHURCH

Main Street at Elizabeth Avenue, Bethlehem.

Archivist: Vernon Nelson

Hours: 8:30 A. M.-12:00 M., 1:30-5:00 P. M., Monday through Friday; 8:30 A. M.-12:00 M., Saturday. Make an appointment if planning extensive use.

HOLDINGS: Approximately 300 cubic feet of manuscript and typescript materials, substantially arranged and partially catalogued. Included are *General Economy Records* (1750-1771), ca. 80 cubic feet, dealing with the farms, forests, crafts, and professions of the Moravians in Northampton County during the period of the Economy (some records, however, extend beyond its cessation in 1762); *Moravian Church Records* (1747-1848), ca. 53 cubic feet of *Gemein-Nachrichten,* reports from the Unity Elders' Conference, and minutes and results of General Synods—*Gemein-Nachrichten* are in effect handwritten newspapers, mostly in German; *Indian Mission Records of the Moravian Church* (1739-1860), ca. 36 cubic feet of letters, missionaries' travel journals, diaries of the missions, etc., mostly in German, which deal with Indians in Pennsylvania, New York, Ohio, Ontario, Kansas, Georgia, and Oklahoma—prominent missionaries include David Zeisberger and John Heckewelder; *Mission Records of the Moravian Church* (1737-present), ca. 36 cubic feet of letters, church books, and fiscal reports of missionaries in Alaska and other areas in North America and the West Indies; *Records of the Moravian Church of Bethlehem* (1742-c. 1900), ca. 30 cubic feet of church records, diaries, and manuscript music, etc., transferred from the Central Moravian Church of Bethlehem; *Records of Individual Moravian Congregations* (1735-1963), ca. 53 cubic feet of church records from congregations in New York, Ohio, Pennsylvania, Minnesota, New Jersey, Rhode Island, Wisconsin, Georgia, Maryland, Indiana, Illinois, Iowa, Kansas, and North Dakota —mostly in German; *John Ettwein Papers* (1762-1799), ca. 2.7 cubic feet of materials of a Moravian bishop who was in charge of missionary activities in Pennsylvania; *Augustus G. Spangenberg Papers* (c. 1739-1785), ca. 1.5 cubic feet of correspondence, etc., amassed in Germany and America by one of Zinzendorf's successors; *Count Nicholas von Zinzendorf Collection* (1719-1760), ca. 2.5 cubic feet of materials which mix copies with original letters; and others.

COPY SERVICES: Photocopying and microfilming can be arranged.

SEE: Kenneth G. Hamilton, "The Moravian Archives at Bethlehem, Pennsylvania," *American Archivist,* XXIV (Oct. 1961), 415-423; and Kenneth G. Hamilton, "The Resources of the Moravian Church Archives," *Pennsylvania History,* XXVII (July, 1960), 263-271. Reprints of both articles are available from the depository.

BETHLEHEM PUBLIC LIBRARY

11 West Market Street, Bethlehem.

Librarian: Miss Amy Preston

Hours: 9:00 A. M.-9:00 P. M., Monday through Friday; 9:00 A. M.-5:00 P. M., Saturday.

HOLDINGS: Approximately 5.75 cubic feet of typescript material, both arranged and indexed. Materials consist of the *Bethlehem Collection* (1742-1939), ca. 4.75 cubic feet of bound volumes of transcripts of church, cemetery, and pastoral records of various denominations in Northampton and Lehigh counties and of all Moravian churches in Pennsylvania; and ca. 1 cubic foot of marriages and deaths extracted from the Bethlehem *Daily Times* (1867-1890).

COPY SERVICES: Photocopies.

LEHIGH UNIVERSITY

Library, Bethlehem.

Librarian: James D. Mack

Hours: 8:00 A. M.-10:00 P. M., Monday through Friday; 8:00 A. M.-5:00 P. M. Saturday.

HOLDINGS: Approximately 1.25 cubic feet of indexed manuscript material including the *Lehigh University Autograph Collection*, ca. 1 cubic foot of letters of both American and European personages, including a set of Presidential autographs and letters of such prominent Americans as Albert Gallatin, John Jay, John C. Calhoun, and Benjamin Franklin; *John R. Bartlett Papers* (1863-1867), ca. .05 cubic foot pertaining to the Soldiers National Cemetery at Gettysburg, including preliminary plans and sketches for the National Monument and correspondence to Bartlett, the state trustee of the Soldiers National Cemetery at Gettysburg from Rhode Island, from Gov. James Smith of Rhode Island, and from David Wills; *Monroe-Hamilton Collection* (1792-1797), ca. .03 cubic foot consisting of 8 documents pertaining to the "Reynolds Affair," including documents by Monroe, Hamilton, and Jacob Clingman.

COPY SERVICES: Photocopies and microfilm.

Bloomsburg

COLUMBIA COUNTY HISTORICAL SOCIETY

853 College Hill, P. O. Box 475, Bloomsburg.

Executive Secretary: Edwin M. Barton

Hours: 9:00 A. M.-5:00 P. M., Monday through Friday; 9:00 A. M.-12:00 M., Saturday. It is wise to make an appointment.

HOLDINGS: Approximately 120 cubic feet of manuscript and typescript, almost entirely unsorted and uncatalogued. The vast preponderance of the collection is business papers of Columbia County firms including *Moyer Brothers Records* (c. 1860-1960), the voluminous records of a retail and manufacturing drug house that was involved in the patent medicine field; *Bloomsburg Iron Company Records* (1840's-1850's); and others.

COPY SERVICES: Photocopying can be arranged.

Bryn Athyn
ACADEMY OF THE NEW CHURCH

Library, Bryn Athyn.

Librarian: Miss Lois Stebbing

Curator of Swedenborgiana: Miss B. G. Briscoe

Hours: By appointment.

HOLDINGS: Approximately 168 cubic feet of manuscript materials, largely arranged and catalogued, in the institution's Archives include the records of the academy (1878-present) and of the New Church (1800-present) and the papers of a number of prominent Swedenborgians. In addition to possessing a few original Swedenborg items, the library has a set, unique in America, of photocopies and transcripts of materials relating to the founder of the New Church.

COPY SERVICES: Microfilm and photocopies.

Carlisle
CUMBERLAND COUNTY HISTORICAL SOCIETY AND HAMILTON LIBRARY ASSOCIATION

21 North Pitt Street, Carlisle.

Librarian: Mrs. John F. Brougher

Hours: 7:00-9:00 P. M., Monday; 1:30-3:30 P. M., Wednesday; 3:00-5:00 P. M., Thursday.

HOLDINGS: Approximately 15 cubic feet of manuscript and typescript materials, neither arranged nor catalogued. Materials are largely dispersed, but there are a number of individual items of interest including letters by James Hamilton, Alexander Hamilton, Fitzhugh Lee, James Buchanan, John Armstrong, and Thomas Cooper. The only collections kept as entities are the *Sylvester B. Sadler Collection* (1768-1830), ca. .65 cubic foot of local county records and financial papers; and the *Jeremiah Zeamer Genealogical Collection,* ca. 3 cubic feet.

COPY SERVICES: Photocopying can be arranged.

DICKINSON COLLEGE

Library, Carlisle.

Librarian: Dr. Charles C. Sellers

Hours: By appointment.

HOLDINGS: Approximately 28 cubic feet of manuscript and typescript materials, largely arranged and catalogued. Included are the *Bowdle Family Papers* (1776-c. 1860), ca. .90 cubic foot of material dealing largely with the attitudes towards slavery of a Maryland family which moved to Cincinnati; *Robert Bridges Papers* (c. 1870-1941), ca. 2.5 cubic feet of materials of a Shippensburg man who became an editor of *Scribner's* and a close friend of Woodrow Wilson; *James Buchanan Collection* (c. 1809-1868), ca. 1.5 cubic feet of letters to and from Buchanan and political letters of the Buchanan period; *John Hastings, Jr., Papers* (c. 1810-c. 1850), ca. .66 cubic foot of materials amassed by a minor New England artist and ink manufacturer; *Charles Francis Himes Papers* (1852-1918), ca. 7.5 cubic feet of papers of a professor of physics at Dickinson who was also a pioneer in photography; *David W. Hulings Papers* (1800-1865), ca. .65 cubic foot of materials amassed by a lawyer from Lewistown who had interests in the iron industry; *Marion D. Learned Papers* (1880-1918), ca. 3 cubic feet of papers of the chairman of the German department of the University of Pennsylvania, who was active in attempts to cement German-American relations; *George Lyon Family Papers* (1780-1840), ca. .66 cubic foot of records of a Carlisle family active in the Presbyterian church, which mirror internal warfare in that institution; *George Peabody Papers* (1847-1855), ca. .30 cubic foot of materials pertaining to a 19th C. philanthropist; *Presidents of the United States Collection*, ca. .25 cubic foot of autograph letters; *James Gordon Steese Papers* (1929-1958), ca. 1 cubic foot of the diaries and other papers amassed during his military and civilian business career; *Slifer-Dill Papers* (c. 1850-1867), ca. 7 cubic feet of the papers of Secretary of the Commonwealth Eli Slifer (1860-1867): most materials are of a political nature.

COPY SERVICES: Photocopies.

Chester

DELAWARE COUNTY HISTORICAL SOCIETY

Old Courthouse, 410-412 Market Street, Chester.

Curator: Mrs. Helen Greenhalgh

Hours: 1:00-4:00 P. M., Monday through Friday; 9:00 A. M.-12:00 M. Saturday (except July). Closed in August.

HOLDINGS: Approximately 31.7 cubic feet of manuscript and typescript materials, partially catalogued and arranged. Included are the *Chester F. Baker Collection* (1904-1960), ca. 13 cubic feet of notes on historical topics, correspondences concerning historical subjects, abstracts from newspapers, and assessments dealing with Delaware County history mixed in with newspaper clippings; *Business Ledgers Collection,* ca. 6 cubic feet, mostly 19th C.; *Deed Collection,* ca. 1.5 cubic feet of mostly Delaware County properties; *Hubley Collection* (1740-1789), ca. .10 cubic foot of Delaware County land records; *Mrs. Kenneth F. Terry Collection* (1710-1786), ca. .10 cubic foot of legal papers of Philadelphia and vicinity; and others.

COPY SERVICES: Microfilming can be arranged.

Collegeville

URSINUS COLLEGE

Alumni Memorial Library, Collegeville.

Librarian: Dr. Calvin D. Yost, Jr.

Hours: Winter: 8:00 A. M.-12:00 M., 12:30-5:00, 6:30-10:00 P. M., Monday through Thursday; 8:00 A. M.-12:00 M., 12:30-5:00 P. M., Friday and Saturday; 12:30-5:00, 6:30-10:00 P. M., Sunday. Summer: 8:30 A. M.-12:00 M., 1:00-4:30 P. M., Monday through Friday.

HOLDINGS: The collection, which is neither indexed nor arranged, consists entirely of the *Huntington Wilson Papers* (c. 1906-1936), ca. 2 cubic feet of papers and memorabilia consisting of incoming letters, copies of outgoing letters, speeches, and fragmentary journals kept in South America (1914) by Wilson, an American diplomat and newspaperman who in his later career took an active part in Republican politics, became violently anti-New Deal and an "America Firster."

COPY SERVICES: Limited photocopies available.

Coudersport

POTTER COUNTY HISTORICAL SOCIETY

308 North Main Street, Coudersport.

Secretary: Mrs. Maybel Swanson

Hours: 2:00-4:00 P. M., Monday and Friday, and by appointment.

HOLDINGS: Approximately 17.50 cubic feet of manuscript and typescript materials, neither arranged nor catalogued. Included are *Deed Collection,* .60 cubic foot; *Education Collection* (1841-1943), ca. 5 cubic feet of Potter County school attendance records and typescript school histories collected and amassed by Mrs. Mary Welfling; *Ledgers and Business Records Collection* (c. 1840-1900), ca. 8 cubic feet; *Pension Claims of Civil War Soldiers,* ca. 1 cubic foot; and others.

COPY SERVICES: **None.**

Doylestown

BUCKS COUNTY HISTORICAL SOCIETY

Pine and Ashland Streets, Doylestown.

Librarian: Mrs. Paul Niemeyer

Hours: 10:00 A. M.-5:00 P. M., Tuesday through Friday.

HOLDINGS: Approximately 225 cubic feet of manuscript and typescript material partially indexed and arranged. Manuscripts include *Blaker Family Papers* (1700-1864), ca. .30 cubic foot consisting of deeds, receipts, mortgage bonds, estate papers, and misc. land records of a Northampton Township family; *Bucks County Township Tax Records* (1782-1930 [1928-1929 missing]), ca. 273 cubic feet; *W. Harry Cadwallader Papers* (c. 1852-1897), ca. .25 cubic foot consisting mainly of records of Civil War relief receipts, County Treasurer's accounts, and mercantile license records kept by an individual prominent in Bucks County politics; *Henry Chapman Papers* (1697-1863), ca. .75 cubic foot which, although it includes a few papers of earlier Chapmans, contains mostly materials pertaining to Henry Chapman's career as a Bucks County lawyer and jurist during the first half of the 19th C.— see also the society's *John Barclay Papers* (Isaac Norris-Henry Chapman correspondence) and *Docket Book Collection* (16 docket books [1790-1865] kept by various members of the Chapman family); *Louis Martial Jacques Crousillat Collection* (1798-c. 1820), ca. .20 cubic foot consisting of receipts, sworn statements, and misc. business papers pertaining to early maritime trade—Crousillat, a Frenchman living in Philadelphia, was the owner of a number of ships engaged in trade with Spain, England, the British West Indies, France, and North Africa. Several of his ships, including the "Nymph" and the "Nancy," were seized by French and Spanish authorities during the Napoleanic Wars; *William Watts Hart Papers* (1767-1910), ca. 6 cubic feet of material collected by and pertaining to Hart, a Civil War colonel (and later desk general), Bucks County historian, author, and commissioner to the Paris Exposition of 1878: the manuscripts include a letter book and records of orders (1861-1864), addresses, personal correspondence, genealogical materials, and notes compiled for his books; *Michael Dech Papers* (1796-1854), ca. 1 cubic foot of business and legal papers of two generations of the Dech family collected by Michael Dech, a 19th C. hat manufacturer; *Charles Du Bois Papers* (1820-1900), ca. .50 cubic foot of mostly legal papers amassed by a Bucks County lawyer; *Durham Iron Works Collection* (1779-1936), ca. 7.2 cubic feet consisting of ca. 30 bound vols. containing daybooks and work books, deeds, letters, and ledgers of a Bucks County iron firm: the majority of the material deals with the 18th C. and early 19th C.; *Samuel C. Eastburn Collection* (1630-1930), ca. 1 cubic foot of material pertaining to the Quakers in the form of manuscripts of historical articles and religious papers, also business correspondence of the collector, Mr. Eastburn (1848-1931), who was a local insurance man; *Foulke Family Papers* (1726-1888), ca. 1.25 cubic feet of land records and land draughts surveyed

9

by members of the Foulke family; *Samuel Hart(s) Papers* (1810-1910), ca. 2 cubic feet of mostly legal documents of a prominent Bucks County father and his son of the same name; *Michael Hutchinson Jenks Collection* (1795-1867), ca. 1.75 cubic feet of early deeds and legal papers and of business letters pertaining to land sales, and estate administration to which Jenks, a lawyer and jurist, was a party; *William B. Kirkbride Collection* (1688-1821), ca. .50 cubic foot of business papers and documents pertaining to land transactions of Kirkbride's ancestors; *Kulp Collection* (1778-1869), ca. .25 cubic foot of business letters and papers of a Bucks County, Pennsylvania-German family; *Mercantile Collection* (c. 1777-1917), ca. 42 cubic feet of material valuable to the study of the region's economic history, including farmers' daybooks, turnpike and canal records, an insurance company and newspaper account books; *John Mercer Ledgers* (1725-1737, 1744-1749), 2 vols. which give a day by day record of his receipts and expenditures as an eminent lawyer and Burgess of Spotsylvania, Virginia, and a list of books in his library; *Philadelphia Fire Company Records* (1832-1917), ca. 24 cubic feet of material consisting of ca. 115 volumes of minute books, membership rolls, and other records; genealogical materials, consisting of ca. 15 cubic feet of church and cemetery records, vital statistics, and family genealogies. Important miscellanea include Edward Hicks' account book; "General Registry" (1684-1685), a small volume consisting of "Letters of Good Conduct" brought to Bucks County by the early arrivals; "Record of Bucks County Ear Marks Entered between the years, 1682-1693," a small volume containing exact drawings of ear marks for cattle; "Minutes of the Committee of Safety, Bucks County" (July 9, 1774-July 29, 1776), one vol.; "Minutes of the several Agreements, Leases and Deeds drawn between the Honorable John Penn, Jun'r and John Penn, Esquires; late Proprietaries of Pennsylvania and the several Purchasers and Leasees therein named . . ." (1784-1790), 1 vol.; and others.

COPY SERVICES: None.

Easton

EASTON PUBLIC LIBRARY

Sixth and Church Streets, Easton.

Librarian: Mrs. Jane S. Moyer

Hours: 1:00-5:00 P. M., Monday, Tuesday, Wednesday, and Friday; 9:00 A. M.-5:00 P. M., Saturday; and by appointment.

HOLDINGS: Approximately 17.5 cubic feet of typescript material both arranged and indexed. Material consists of the *Library Collection* (1752-1886), ca. 14 cubic feet of local church records, ca. 1 cubic foot of abstracts of wills of Northampton County (1752-1840), and ca. 2.5 cubic feet of marriages and deaths abstracted from local newspapers (1799-1886).

COPY SERVICES: Certified copies and photocopies.

LAFAYETTE COLLEGE

Kirby Library, Easton.

Librarian: Clyde Haselen

Hours: 8:30 A. M.-12:00 M., Monday through Friday; 9:00 A. M.-5:00 P. M., Saturday; 2:00-5:00, 7:00-12:00 P. M., Sunday during the regular academic year. It is wise, however, to make an appointment.

HOLDINGS: Approximately 2.5 cubic feet of arranged manuscripts. Included are the *Lafayette Collection* (1777-1831), ca. 2 cubic feet of letters and contemporary unsigned copies of letters written by the Marquis de Lafayette: included in the collection are 136 letters written to George Washington (1777-1797), letters written to Vergennes, and the original MS of his address to Congress given in 1824; and miscellaneous letters including items by George Washington (1767), John Jay (1779), and John Sullivan (1779).

COPY SERVICES: None.

NORTHAMPTON COUNTY HISTORICAL AND GENEALOGICAL SOCIETY

101 South Fourth Street, Easton.

Librarian: Mrs. Jane S. Moyer

Hours: 7:00-10:00 P. M., Thursday and Friday, and by appointment. Address correspondence regarding library's use to above; all other to Russell Baver, secretary.

HOLDINGS: Approximately 18 cubic feet of manuscript and typescript materials, partially arranged and indexed, including *Society Miscellaneous Collection* (1734-1942), ca. 5 cubic feet including personal and business papers and Civil War and Revolutionary War muster rolls; *Deeds* (1790-1868), ca. 2 cubic feet; *Account and Ledger Books* (19th C.), ca. 4 cubic feet consisting of some 80 volumes; and others.

COPY SERVICES: None.

Elverson

HOPEWELL VILLAGE NATIONAL HISTORIC PARK

R. F. D. 1, Elverson.

Superintendent: Benjamin J. Zerbey

Hours: 9:30 A. M.-5:30 P. M., daily except Christmas. Make an appointment if planning extensive use.

HOLDINGS: Approximately 36 cubic feet of manuscript material almost completely arranged and catalogued. Holdings include the *Hopewell Furnace Records* (1784-1896), ca. 30 cubic feet consisting of the

11

furnace account books (1800-1896), and some 7,000 letters which deal with the furnace and the early history of Birdsboro;* *Eckert & Co. Furnaces Collection* (1867-1894), ca. 2 cubic feet consisting of 7 volumes which document the company's operation in and around Reading; *Birdsboro Forge Account Books* (1800-1810), ca. 2 cubic feet consisting of 10 volumes; *Farmers Bank of Reading Collection* (1814-1830's), ca. 1.25 cubic feet consisting of 15 record books and several miscellaneous items.

COPY SERVICES: Photocopies available.

---

* Other Hopewell Furnace account books are at the Historical Society of Berks County, Reading; the Chester County Historical Society, West Chester; and the Historical Society of Pennsylvania, Philadelphia.

Erie

ERIE COUNTY HISTORICAL SOCIETY

Old Customs House, 407 State Street, Erie.

Secretary: Mrs. Frances Epp

Hours: 1:30-5:00 P. M., Monday through Friday. Address correspondence to the society.

HOLDINGS: Approximately 4.5 cubic feet of manuscript and typescript materials, which are partially arranged but not catalogued. Included are *Joseph S. Day Papers* (1839-1887), ca. .10 cubic foot of official papers dealing with Day's naval career and his widow's efforts to secure a pension; *Minutes of the Trustees of the Erie Academy* (1900-1916), ca. .20 cubic foot; *Erie City Passenger Railway Collection* (1878-1886), ca. .15 cubic foot of letters, cancelled checks, deeds, and other business papers; *Erie County Tavern Petitions* (1820-1876), ca. 1 cubic foot of petitions for tavern licenses in Erie County; *Old Customs House Collection* (1836), ca. .01 cubic foot, six letters, including one from Nicholas Biddle to Peter Benson, 1st cashier of the Erie office of the Bank of the United States; interesting miscellaneous items include the George A. Olmstead diaries (1872-1874), kept by a farmer living near Corry, Pennsylvania; several Josiah Kellog letters dealing with land transactions and banking in Erie; John Grubb orderly book (May 11-Aug. 24, 1795); a Daniel Webster letter (1838); Brig. Major Samuel Douglas orderly book (Oct.-Nov., 1812); and others.

COPY SERVICES: Photocopying can be arranged.

ERIE PUBLIC MUSEUM

Sixth and Chestnut Streets, Erie.

Director: John V. Alexick

Hours: 10:00 A. M.-5:00 P. M., Tuesday through Friday; 2:00-5:00 P. M., Sunday. Correspondence should be addressed to the Director, 356 West 6th Street, Erie.

HOLDINGS: Deal predominantly with Erie and Erie County. Most are arranged and catalogued. Included are *Thomas Foster Papers* (1800-1860), which include port records (1800-1823) and an assessment book of the East Ward of Erie (1860) ; *Laura G. Sanford Papers,* materials including her family papers collected by an Erie historian, business records, War of 1812 papers, etc.; *Frances L. Spenser Papers,* materials include Pennsylvania Population Company papers and Judah Colt papers; and others.

COPY SERVICES: Microfilming and photocopying can be arranged.

Franklin

VENANGO COUNTY HISTORICAL SOCIETY
Franklin Public Library, Franklin.

Archivist: Mrs. Charles A. Morrison

Hours: 2:00-4:00 P. M., Tuesday and Saturday; and by appointment. Direct inquiries to Mrs. Morrison, R. F. D. 2, Franklin.

HOLDINGS: Approximately 2.3 cubic feet of manuscript and typescript materials, neither arranged nor catalogued. Included are *Account Books and Ledger Collection* (1818-1951), ca. 1.15 cubic feet of volumes relating to Venango County enterprises; *W. B. Mays Post 220 G.A.R. Collection* (1862-1929), ca. .60 cubic foot consisting of roll books, minutes, and other records of the organization; *John Hamilton Papers* (1814-1823), ca. .25 cubic foot of legal papers amassed during his tenure of office as sheriff of Venango County, and a ledger of his general store; miscellaneous items of interest include several early cemetery records, United States postal money order book from Pithole (1866-1869), several letters written by General Samuel P. Hays (1812-1855), etc.; and others.

COPY SERVICES: Typescripts.

Gettysburg

ADAMS COUNTY HISTORICAL SOCIETY
Old Dorm, Lutheran Theological Seminary, Gettysburg.

Corresponding Secretary: Arthur Weaner

Hours: By appointment. Address correspondence to Mr. Weaner, R. F. D. 6, Box 320, Gettysburg.

HOLDINGS: Approximately 26 cubic feet of manuscript materials, largely uncatalogued and unarranged. Included are *Local Union 316, Cigar Makers Union, McSherrytown, Papers* (c. 1898-1950), ca. 6 cubic feet of ledgers, membership rolls, and other records; *William Archibald McClean Collection* (1817-1889), ca. .75 cubic foot of legal papers and items dealing with Gettysburg College amassed by a Gettysburg attorney and judge who specialized in estate work; *Ledgers Collection,* ca. 4 cubic feet of 19th C. records, public and private, including those of the Adams County Poor House; *Family Records,* ca. 6 cubic feet of files containing manuscript and typescript materials mixed with printed matter; *Abstracts of Adams County Cemetery Records and Burial Permits,* ca. 5.5 cubic feet of 3″ x 5″ index cards arranged by cemeteries; miscellaneous items include letters by Thaddeus Stevens, James Buchanan, Simon Cameron, Stephen A. Douglas, etc.; and others.

COPY SERVICES: No set policy.

GETTYSBURG COLLEGE

Civil War Institute, Gettysburg.

Director: John H. Knickerbocker

Hours: 9:00 A. M.-5:00 P. M., Monday through Friday, and by appointment. It is advisable to make an appointment at all times.

HOLDINGS: Approximately .35 cubic foot of manuscript materials, arranged and catalogued, pertaining to the Civil War, esp. the Battle of Gettysburg, and the establishment of the National Military Park. Included are letters by Robert E. Lee, General George G. Meade, and Andrew Gregg Curtin.

COPY SERVICES: Photocopies.

GETTYSBURG COLLEGE

Schmucker Memorial Library, Gettysburg.

Librarian: Mrs. Kenneth L. Smoke

Hours: Academic year: 8:30 A. M.-11:30 P. M., Monday through Friday; 8:30 A. M.- 5:00 P. M., Saturday; 1:30-11:30 P. M., Sunday. Summer session; 9:00 A. M.-5:00 P. M., Monday through Friday; 9:00 A. M.-1:00 P. M., Saturday. Vacations and intersessions, except special holidays: 9:00 A. M.-12:00 M.

HOLDINGS: A small collection of manuscripts, largely arranged and indexed, which pertain principally to the founding and development of Gettysburg College. Included are letters of Samuel S. Schmucker, Michael Jacobs, Thaddeus Stevens, Edward McPherson, J. H. W. Stuckenberg, and others, including single items from Daniel Webster and Herbert Hoover. There is also a small collection of World War I letters.

COPY SERVICES: Photocopies.

LUTHERAN THEOLOGICAL SEMINARY

Library, Gettysburg.

Librarian: Dr. Herbert H. Schmidt

Hours: 8:30 A. M.-5:00 P. M., Monday through Friday.

HOLDINGS: Approximately 53.50 cubic feet of manuscript and typescript materials, partially arranged. Included are the *Notes of the*

Board of Education of the Lutheran Student Association (1921-1946), ca. 34 cubic feet of records of, and correspondence pertaining to collegiate centers maintained by the Church on campuses throughout the country (on deposit from the Lutheran Student Association, Washington, D. C.); *Church Records of Defunct Churches of the Central Pennsylvania Synod,* ca. 10 cubic feet (on deposit from the Central Pennsylvania Synod Office); *Gabriel Adam Reichert Collection* (1821-1854), ca. .25 cubic foot of a Lutheran minister and missionary's diaries and sermon notes in German; *Samuel Simon Schmucker Collection* (c. 1820-1877), ca. .25 cubic foot of letters, sermons, and lecture notes of a prominent educator who was a founder of both this institution and Gettysburg College; *Synod Records,* ca. 5 cubic feet, including those of the Evangelical Lutheran Synod of Maryland (1903-1916) and the Western Pennsylvania Synod (1840-1921); miscellaneous items of interest include several Muhlenberg letters, one written in 1747 to Conrad Weiser; and others.

COPY SERVICES: Photocopying can be arranged.

Greenville

THIEL COLLEGE

Langenheim Memorial Library, Greenville.

College Librarian and Archivist, United Lutheran Church of America: Ray Dunmire

Hours: 8:00 A. M.-5:00 P. M., Monday through Saturday; Sunday by appointment. It is wise, however, to make an appointment.

HOLDINGS: Approximately 23 cubic feet of manuscript materials, almost entirely arranged and catalogued. Included are *Manuscript Church Record Books* (1788-1949) of Lutheran churches in the Pittsburgh Synod of the Evangelical Lutheran Church, which includes, besides western Pennsylvania, portions of Ohio and West Virginia; *Records of the Lutheran Ministerial Association of Pittsburgh* (1913-1919); *Records of the Western Pennsylvania and West Virginia Synod* (formerly Pittsburgh Synod) *of the Evangelical Lutheran Church* (1845-present), which includes financial records (1881-1901), protocol minutes (1845-1919), minutes of the Advisory Board of Home Missions (1899-1919), Executive Committee minutes (1895-present), Education Committee minute book (1886-1892), Lutheran Brotherhood correspondence and minutes, etc.; *Records of the General Council of the Western Pennsylvania and West Virginia Synod* (formerly Pittsburgh Synod) *of the Evangelical Lutheran Church* (1867-1919); *Records of the Western Pennsylvania and West Virginia Synod* (formerly Pittsburgh Synod) *Conferences* (1863-present), which includes minutes, proceedings, protocol books, and constitutions of the various conferences held within the Synod; *Gottlieb Bassler Papers* (1836-1866) includes 5 journals, 31 letters to Henry Muntz, and convention minutes of a prominent Lutheran; just acquired, and in process of preparation are papers of Carroll D. Kearns, member of Congress from the 24th Congressional District of Pennsylvania (1947-1963); and others.

COPY SERVICES: Photocopies.

Harrisburg

HISTORICAL SOCIETY OF DAUPHIN COUNTY

219 South Front Street, Harrisburg.

Curator: Mrs. John Tillman

Hours: 1:00-5:00 P. M., Monday through Friday; 1:00-4:00 P. M., Saturday. Closed Saturday during July and August.

HOLDINGS: Approximately 24 cubic feet of manuscript material. Included are the *Bucher Papers* (1761-1849), ca. 1.9 cubic feet consisting of sermon notes, materials relating to building the Harrisburg Bridge and public buildings, and court records from Dauphin, Cumberland, and Lancaster counties—a portion of the papers are in German; *Simon Cameron Papers* (1836-1892), ca. 4 cubic feet consisting of mostly incoming letters and business papers of a major figure in Pennsylvania politics; *Dr. William R. DeWitt Collection,* ca. .10 cubic foot of papers of the Chief Medical Officer of the Union Army during the Civil War; *Casper Dull Papers* (1840-1863), ca. .05 cubic foot—mostly Civil War material; *John Elder Papers* (1742-1843), ca. 1.35 cubic feet of materials including sermon notes, business and military papers, and records of the Dauphin County prothonotary; *Kelker Collection* (1794-1906), ca. .10 cubic foot of legal and tax records and records of a hardware store; *Shirk Records,* ca. 6 cubic feet of genealogical data; *Joseph Wallace Papers* (1812-1854), ca. .05 cubic foot of business records of New Market Forge, Lebanon, Pennsylvania; interesting miscellanea include the John Harris lot book and deeds; and others.

COPY SERVICES: Photocopying and microfilming can be arranged.

PENNSYLVANIA HISTORICAL AND MUSEUM COMMISSION

Division of Public Records, William Penn Memorial Museum and Archives Building, Harrisburg.

Division Chief: William H. Work

Hours: 8:30 A. M.-5:00 P. M., Monday through Friday.

HOLDINGS: In addition to the public records of the Commonwealth of Pennsylvania, which currently total more than 15,000 cubic feet, there are approximately 300 cubic feet of manuscript and typescript materials, almost entirely arranged and catalogued. Included are *Burd Family Papers* (1815-1833), ca. 1 cubic foot consisting chiefly of transcribed correspondence and accounts of Col. James Burd and his sons and relatives; *Edward Shippen Thompson Collection* (1746-1890), ca. 4 cubic feet of materials from and about Col. James Burd and his family and their activities, centering mainly in Dauphin and Juniata counties; *Schuylkill Navigation Company Books and Papers* (1793-1944), ca. 150 cubic feet and 3 reels of microfilm, which consist of reports, minute books, accounts, correspondence, and other papers and records of an important canal company; and others.

COPY SERVICES: Photocopies and microfilm.

SEE: *Preliminary Guide to the Research Materials of the Pennsylvania Historical and Museum Commission,* Harrisburg: PHMC, 1959.

Haverford

HAVERFORD COLLEGE

Library, Haverford.

Curator: Prof. Edwin B. Bronner

Hours: Academic year: 9:00 A. M.-12:30 P. M., 1:30-4:30 P. M., Monday through Friday. Summer: 1:30-4:30 P. M., Tuesday and Friday, and by appointment. Closed August.

HOLDINGS: Approximately 525 cubic feet of manuscript and typescript materials, largely arranged and indexed. The holdings are divided into two major collections: The *Quaker Collection* (1660-1962), ca. 305 cubic feet, which includes letters of William Penn, George Fox, John G. Whittier, John Woolman, the papers of Rufus M. Jones, family papers of many early Pennsylvania and New Jersey Quaker families, 700 manuscript journals, much material on Friends and the Indians, including records of the Lake Mohonk Conference of Friends of the Indians (1883-1929), collections on Friends and reform movements, and official papers of Friends' Yearly Meetings and other bodies; and the *Charles Roberts Collection* (1480-1962), ca. 220 cubic feet of materials, the nucleus of which is the Charles Roberts Autograph Collection of 12,000 letters, to which the college has added all non-Quaker manuscript materials acquired: the present collection includes two sets of documents of the Signers among its rich holdings of the Revolutionary period, hundreds of letters from the Civil War era, papers connected with the history of Haverford College, and the Miscellaneous Manuscript Collection. The Archives of the American Friends Service Committee (1917-1962), ca. 1,200 cubic feet, are also in the Haverford College Library and are available under special conditions.

COPY SERVICES: Photocopies and microfilm.

SEE: Thomas E. Drake, *The Quaker Collection at Haverford,* Haverford: Haverford College, 1956; *The Quaker Collection of the Haverford College Library,* Haverford: Haverford College, 1963.

Honesdale

WAYNE COUNTY HISTORICAL SOCIETY

810 Main Street, Honesdale.

Secretary: Mrs. Florence Pragnell

Hours: 10:00 A. M.-12:00 M., 1:00-4:00 P. M., Tuesday, Wednesday, Thursday, and Saturday.

HOLDINGS: Approximately 40 cubic feet of manuscript and typescript materials, neither arranged nor catalogued. A project is under way to rectify this situation. Holdings include papers of Philip Hone, New York businessman, the Delaware and Hudson Canal, a local gravity railroad; and others.

COPY SERVICES: Microfilming and photocopying can be arranged.

Huntingdon

JUNIATA COLLEGE

Library, Eighteenth and Moore Streets, Huntingdon.

Librarian: Mrs. Sarah Hettinger

Hours: 7:45 A. M.-5:00 P. M., 7:00-10:00 P. M., Monday through Friday.

HOLDINGS: Approximately 3.5 cubic feet of manuscript and typescript materials, which are almost entirely arranged and catalogued. The largest single collection is the *John Cadwallader Papers* (1790-1821), ca. .35 cubic foot of personal correspondence and business papers of an early Huntingdon lawyer who was its first postmaster, the owner of a paper mill at Birmingham, Pa., a local official, and a Mason. There are a number of miscellaneous items of interest, including several Christopher Saur items, the records of the overseers of the poor and other local records (1748-1814) of Salford Township in Montgomery County, and several small account books and ledgers of a brick burner in Schuylkill County.

COPY SERVICES: None.

Indiana

HISTORICAL AND GENEALOGICAL SOCIETY OF INDIANA COUNTY

Memorial Hall, Indiana.

Librarian: Mrs. Frances Strong Helman

Hours: 1:30-4:00, 6:30-9:00 P. M., Tuesday and Thursday, except holidays. Address correspondence to the society at large.

HOLDINGS: Approximately 19 cubic feet of manuscript and typescript materials, mostly arranged but not catalogued. Included are the *Genealogy File,* ca. 6 cubic feet of abstracted information from local papers and wills, etc., recorded on 3" x 5" index cards; *Family Material File,* manuscript and typescript materials combined with printed materials in files occupying ca. 12 cubic feet; there are also miscellaneous local cemetery records, a few Civil War items, etc.; and others.

COPY SERVICES: None.

Lancaster

FRANKLIN AND MARSHALL COLLEGE

Fackenthal Library, West James Street and College Avenue, Lancaster.

Librarian: Herbert Anstaett

Hours: 8:00 A. M.-12:00 M., 1:00-5:00 P. M., Monday through Friday.

HOLDINGS: Approximately 75.25 cubic feet of manuscript and type-script materials, largely arranged and catalogued. Holdings include *Jonathan Messersmith Foltz Diaries* (1831-1877), ca. 1.4 cubic feet consisting of material giving details of naval life centering on the Mississippi Valley Campaign of the Civil War, and Foltz's later services as surgeon general of the United States Navy; *Irwin Hoch De Long Collection,* ca. 2 cubic feet of genealogical materials; *Linnaean Society of Lancaster Collection* (1862-1894), ca. .50 cubic foot of manuscript materials pertaining to this scientific organization; the *Pennsylvania Folklife Society Collection,* ca. 52 cubic feet of genealogical materials consisting of ca. 150,000 card entries on Pennsylvania Germans; *Reynolds Family Papers* (1830-1865), ca. 2 cubic feet of manuscripts and other materials collected by the family of General John Fulton Reynolds and William Reynolds, which includes correspondence from James Buchanan and Harriet Lane, and letters of condolence from Abraham Lincoln, General George Meade, and other Civil War notables; *David McNeely Stauffer Papers* (1845-1910), ca. .25 cubic foot consisting of several diaries and a manuscript autobiography of a Lancaster County-born engineer who worked on many railroad projects; *Claude W. Unger Collection,* ca. 10 cubic feet of genealogical notes, church, and cemetery records, and family cards; and others.

COPY SERVICES: Photocopies.

HISTORICAL SOCIETY OF THE EVANGELICAL AND REFORMED CHURCH

Fackenthal Library, Franklin and Marshall College, Lancaster.

Archivist: Miss Elizabeth Kieffer

Hours: 10:30 A. M.-2:30 P. M., Monday through Friday, and by appointment. It is always best, however, to make an appointment.

HOLDINGS: Approximately 54 cubic feet of manuscript and typescript materials in addition to 72 cubic feet of church archives. The materials are mostly arranged and catalogued. Holdings include *Henry*

Sassaman Dotterer Collection (15th-17th C.), ca. .50 cubic foot of transcriptions of, and abstractions from European sources which include materials pertaining to the Church in America; *William John Hinke Collection* (1693-1816), ca. 9.5 cubic feet of materials, including transcripts of church records, diaries, and personal letters of ministers, etc., gathered from both American and European sources; *Papers of Reformed Church Ministers* (1745-present), ca. 17 cubic feet of correspondence, sermons, and manuscript articles; *Reformed Church Diaries* (1777-1918), ca. 7 cubic feet of material, much of it pertaining to the Civil War period; and others.

COPY SERVICES: Photocopies.

SEE: Elizabeth Kieffer, "Genealogical Resources of the Historical Society of the Evangelical and Reformed Church, Fackenthal Library, Franklin and Marshall College, Lancaster, Pennsylvania," *National Genealogical Society Quarterly,* XLVIII (Sept. 1960). Reprints are available at the society.

LANCASTER COUNTY HISTORICAL SOCIETY

230 North President Avenue, Lancaster.

Librarian: Mrs. Charles W. Lundgren

Hours: 1:00-5:00 P. M., Monday, Tuesday, Wednesday, Friday, and Sunday; 1:00-5:00, 7:00-10:00 P. M., Thursday; 10:00 A. M.-5:00 P. M., Saturday.

HOLDINGS: Approximately 345 cubic feet of manuscript and typescript material, partially arranged and catalogued, pertaining mostly to Lancaster County and vicinity. Holdings include the *Edmund Hayes Bell Collection* (18th C.-1920's), ca. 7 cubic feet of materials compiled for and closely related to Mr. Bell's book, *James Patterson of Conestoga Manor and His Descendants; Business Records Collection* (18th and 19th C.), ca. 28 cubic feet of business ledgers and daybooks of local turnpikes and other establishments; *Lancaster County Assessment Books* (1730-1939), ca. 260 cubic feet; *Joseph Hubley Manuscripts* (1745-1811), ca. .25 cubic foot consisting mainly of business papers of a Lancaster County family; *David Lynch Correspondence* (1834-1860), ca. .25 cubic foot consisting of 175 letters written by Lynch mostly to James Buchanan concerning Pennsylvania politics; *McCaa Papers* (mid-19th C.), ca. 1 cubic foot of records of a Caernarvon Township physician and justice of the peace; *Adam Reigart Manuscripts* (1796-1879), ca. .25 cubic foot of the business papers of the two Lancaster County merchants named Adam Reigart, who had interests in a mill, drygoods, and the wine and liquor trade; *Thaddeus Stevens Collection* (1848-1868), ca. .15 cubic foot consisting of 18 letters; *Society Miscellaneous Collection* (1700-1891), ca. 1 cubic foot of miscellaneous material including letters, journals, and legal documents arranged in chronological order; *Deed Collection* (1740's-mid-19th C.), ca. 4 cubic feet of partially arranged material; 34 cubic feet of typescript genealogical materials consisting of cemetery records, family histories, and vital statistics abstracts; a few Buchanan articles; and others.

COPY SERVICES: Photocopying can be arranged.

Laporte

SULLIVAN COUNTY HISTORICAL SOCIETY

Laporte.

Secretary: Mrs. K. G. Shelley

Hours: 1:30-5:00 P. M., Saturday from Decoration Day to Labor Day; and by appointment. Direct inquiries to the Secretary, Forksville.

HOLDINGS: Approximately one cubic foot of manuscript and typescript material, almost entirely catalogued. Holdings included 2 justice of the peace dockets, one of which, Edward I. Eldred's, covers 1808 to 1846; Cherry Township assessment book (1847); a memoir of Secku Meylert (1784-1849), an early settler of Sullivan County who was also related to the Rothschilds, written by his son; and others.

COPY SERVICES: Photocopying can be arranged.

Lebanon

LEBANON COUNTY HISTORICAL SOCIETY

Sixth and Walnut Streets, Lebanon.

Assistant Secretary-Curator: Ray S. Bowman

Hours: 1:00-5:00, 7:00-9:00 P. M., Monday except holidays. It is wise to make an appointment. Address correspondence to above, or to Mrs. Robert Clarke, genealogist.

HOLDINGS: Approximately 166 cubic feet of manuscript and typescript materials, only slightly arranged and catalogued. Included are *Business Records Collection* (19th C.), ca. 30 cubic feet of ledgers, turnpike records, justice of the peace dockets, etc.; *Cornwall Furnace Records* (1848-1923), ca. 120 cubic feet of business records—daybooks, cash books, blast books, provision accounts, ore books, time books, receipts, ledgers, pig iron books, etc.—of both Cornwall Furnace and other of the Coleman family enterprises (Colebrook Furnace and Robesonia Iron Company, Limited); *Deed Collection* (18th and 19th C.), ca. 6 cubic feet of mostly Lebanon County documents; *Genealogical Collection,* ca. 9 cubic feet of family histories, etc.; *William K. Lehman Diaries* (1841-1881), ca. 1 cubic foot of small diaries kept by a canal superintendent on the Union Canal who lived in a number of communities including Harrisburg and Lebanon; and others.

COPY SERVICES: Photocopying can be arranged.

Lewisburg

BUCKNELL UNIVERSITY

Ellen Clarke Bertrand Library, Lewisburg.

Librarian in charge of Archives: Mrs. Margaret M. Hayden

Hours: 7:50 A. M.-11:00 P. M., Monday through Friday; 7:50 A .M.-5:00 P. M., Saturday; 2:00-11:00 P. M., Sunday.

HOLDINGS: Approximately 88 cubic feet of manuscript, typescript, and unique microfilm material, substantially arranged and catalogued. Included are *Benjamin K. Focht Papers* (1900-1934), ca. 22 cubic feet of the political papers of the editor of the Lewisburg *Saturday News,* who also served as a member of Congress for a number of years—among the papers are letters from Ida Tarbell, Franklin D. Roosevelt, Herbert Hoover, Henry Morganthau, Jr., etc.; *Bucknell University Autograph Collection,* ca. .50 cubic foot including letters by Albert Einstein, Franklin D. and Eleanor Roosevelt, Will Hays, John Redman Coxe, Adam Kuhn, etc.; *Deed and Indenture Collection,* ca. 18 cubic feet of largely 18th C. documents from Union and Northumberland counties; *Geddes Family Papers* (1817-1871), ca. .50 cubic foot of materials pertaining to a prominent Union County family, one of whose members, James, was a local tax collector; *David Jayne Hill Papers* (1866-1930), ca. 10 cubic feet of the papers and an unpublished autobiography of the president of Bucknell (1879-1888), president of the University of Rochester (1888-1896), and who then entered government service and was asst. secretary of state, and United States minister to Switzerland and the Netherlands, and ambassador to Germany; *Andrew A. Leiser Collection* (1870's-1944), 9 cubic feet of legal papers and ledgers of Andrew A. Leiser, senior and junior, both prominent Lewisburg attorneys, and the letters and documents they amassed concerning the related Leiser-Albright families (1880-1930); *Lewisburg and Mifflinburg Turnpike Collection* (c. 1834-1903), ca. 1.25 cubic feet of account books and other business records; *Minutes and Records of the Lewisburg Civic Club* (1907-1950), ca. 1.25 cubic feet; *James Merrill Linn Papers* (1844-1887), ca. 3 cubic feet, consisting of 11 diaries (1844-1864), 367 letters written to and from his brother John Blair Linn and others (1861-1864), and miscellaneous professional papers of a prominent Lewisburg attorney who served as a captain of Co. H, 51st Regt. Pa. Volun.; *James Moore, II, Diary* (1845-1855), ca. .80 cubic foot, 8-vol. diary kept by the first treasurer of Bucknell who was also a local businessman, prominent Baptist layman, and temperance advocate; *E. B. Riehl Diaries* (1883-1924), ca. 2 cubic feet consisting of 40 small volumes depicting life in Lewisburg; *John Abbet Walls Papers* (1898-1958), ca. 7 cubic feet of mostly business correspondence, including 166 reels of microfilm of business papers (1905-1955) destroyed after microfilming, which relates to the hydro-electric development of the Susquehanna River by the Pennsylvania Water and Power Company, Safe Harbor Water Power Corporation, and the Shawinigan Water and Power Company, and to John

E. Aldred, founder and president of the three companies (collection partially restricted until 1970); related to the John Walls papers are the *Slifer-Walls Papers* (1760-1956), ca. 10 feet of correspondence, personal and business, and genealogical records of the Walls, Slifer, Abbott, Adlum, Frick, and Green families, including diaries and Civil War period letters of Secretary of the Commonwealth Eli Slifer (1861-1867), business records of William C. Wall's mercantile enterprise in Lewisburg, and a diary kept on a trip to California by Robert Green in 1849; *Shorkley Family Papers* (1861-1958), ca. 2.5 cubic feet of materials of a prominent Lewisburg family which had close relations with Bucknell: among the papers are military records, 4-vol. Civil War diary (1861-1865), and other papers of George Shorkley, 1st. Lt., Co. H, 51st Regt., Pa. Volun. (1861-1865), Capt. U. S. 15th Infantry (1866-1885), 8-vol. diary of Elisha Shorkley (1859-1866), Lewisburg businessman, 3-vol. diary of Sarah R. Meixell (1862-1869), family genealogies, etc.; and others.

COPY SERVICES: Photocopies.

SEE: *Bibleotheca Bucknellensis,* a periodical which lists and often describes acquisitions by the library.

Lewistown

MIFFLIN COUNTY HISTORICAL SOCIETY, INC.

Municipal Building, Lewistown.

Librarian: Mrs. J. Martin Stroup

Hours: 7:00-9:00 P. M., Monday and Thursday. It is wise to make an appointment. Correspondence should be addressed to the Corresponding Secretary, J. Martin Stroup, 53 North Pine Street, Lewistown.

HOLDINGS: Approximately 8.5 cubic feet of manuscript and typescript materials partially arranged but not indexed. Holdings include the *Genealogical File,* ca. 6 cubic feet of materials dealing with Mifflin County families, and a number of miscellaneous items including several Hope Furnace (1826-1840) items and the minutes of McVeytown Boro (1833-1894); and others.

COPY SERVICES: Photocopying can be arranged.

Lincoln University

LINCOLN UNIVERSITY

Vail Memorial Library, Lincoln University, Pennsylvania.

Librarian: Dr. Donald C. Yelton

Hours: Academic year: 9:00 A. M.-10:00 P. M., Monday through Friday; 9:00 A. M.-12:30 P. M., Saturday; 7:00-9:00 P. M., Sunday. Summer: 9:00 A. M.-5:00 P. M., Monday through Friday.

HOLDINGS: Eight manuscript volumes, consisting of the *Pennsylvania Colonization Society Papers* (1838-1912), which are made up of 6 volumes of minutes (Jan. 2, 1838-Dec. 11, 1849, July 15, 1856-Jan. 28, 1913), and 1 volume containing the constitution, by-laws, and lists of early members and officers; and *Minutes of the Executive Committee of the Young Men's Colonization Society of Pennsylvania* (June 10, 1834-Feb. 9, 1841).

COPY SERVICES: Photocopies.

Meadville

ALLEGHENY COLLEGE

Reis Library, Meadville.

Librarian: Philip M. Benjamin

Hours: 8:30 A. M.-5:00 P. M., Monday through Friday.

HOLDINGS: Approximately 43 cubic feet of manuscript and typescript materials, mostly arranged and catalogued. Included are the *Arthur L. Bates Papers* (1900-1934), ca. 1.5 cubic feet of speeches and correspondence of a Meadville lawyer who also served as a United States congressman: the papers include letters from Woodrow Wilson, Theodore Roosevelt, and William McKinley, and a single Lincoln letter acquired by the Bates family; *Samuel P. Bates Papers* (1850-1902), ca. .25 cubic foot of correspondence and other papers of a Meadville educator who was the father of Arthur L. Bates; *John Earle Reynolds Collection,* ca. 3 cubic feet of the still unsorted papers of a community and business leader who died in 1942 and who had a substantial interest in the Atlantic and Great Western Railroad; *Ida Tarbell Papers* (1890-1943), ca. 33 cubic feet consisting of about 10,000 items, which includes correspondence with well-known persons and manuscripts of her historical writings—about half of the collection is made up of materials she collected for her Lincoln biography; *Bishop James Mill Thoburn Diaries* (1859-1912), ca .3 cubic feet, kept by the first Methodist bishop in India; and others.

COPY SERVICES: Photocopies available.

CRAWFORD COUNTY HISTORICAL SOCIETY

848 North Main Street, Meadville.

Secretary: Halver W. Getchell

Hours: 1:00-5:00 P. M., Tuesday through Saturday. Address correspondence to the society at large.

HOLDINGS: Approximately 32 cubic feet of manuscript and typescript materials, mostly arranged and catalogued. Included are the *Bank of Western Pennsylvania Papers* (1814-1825), ca. .2 cubic foot of letters, accounts, and receipts; *Business and Legal Record Book Collection* (1792-1904), ca. 17.5 cubic feet; *Cemetery Index,* ca. .50 cubic foot of materials recorded in a continuing operation indexing the occupants of Crawford County cemeteries; *David Dick Letters* (1809-1872), ca. 1.50 cubic feet of correspondence of an early Meadville inventor-engineer and his family, which provide valuable information about the social and economic conditions of the area; *Holland Land Company Papers* (1796-c. 1835), ca. .25 cubic foot consisting of three ledgers, correspondence, and maps—also in this grouping are materials relating to the North American Land Company, Pennsylvania Population Company, and the Donation Lands; *Frederick and Alfred Huidekoper Letter Books* (1855-1890), ca. 3 cubic feet of records of outgoing correspondence of the sons of the elder Huidekoper, an important agent of the Holland Land Company—Frederick was a Unitarian minister who founded the now defunct Meadville Theological Seminary, and Alfred was a prominent businessman; *Meadville Allegheny and Brokenstraw Plank Road Company Records* (1849-1856), ca. .1 cubic foot including accounts and correspondence; *John Earle Reynolds Collection* (1795-1846), ca. 1.1 cubic feet including papers of the Mifflin family (Gov. Thomas Mifflin), of Judge Henry Baldwin, a United States Supreme Court justice whose correspondents included Andrew Jackson, John Tyler, and James Buchanan, of George Croghan, of David Meade, and of Thomas R. Kennedy, a pioneer physician in Western Pennsylvania who also had a number of business interests: *Society Miscellaneous Letter Collection* (1777-1930), ca. 2.5 cubic feet of letters of prominent personages, mostly local; *Susquehanna and Waterford Turnpike Company Records* (1818-1827), ca. .2 cubic foot consisting of one account and two subscription books; *Mrs. Minnie Trapani Collection,* ca. 2 cubic feet of genealogical materials gathered by Mrs. Trapani, which includes vital statistics abstracted from local newspapers (1809-1940) —closely related to this is a file devoted to vital statistics abstracted from local church and courthouse records; *Genealogical Collection,* ca. 2.5 cubic feet of local family histories; interesting miscellanea include three William A. Irvine letters (1848-1849) and the Civil War diaries of William W. Eastman, Band, 28th Regt. of N. Y. Volun. (1862-1863) ; and others.

COPY SERVICES: Photocopies and microfilm.

Mercer

MERCER COUNTY HISTORICAL SOCIETY, INC.

119 South Pitt Street, Mercer.

Assistant Director-Curator: Mrs. James R. Patterson

Hours: 1:00-4:30 P. M., Tuesday through Saturday; 7:00-9:00 P. M. Friday.

HOLDINGS: Approximately 32.50 cubic feet of manuscript and typescript materials neither arranged nor catalogued. Included are the *William Amberson Collection* (1794-1835), ca. .10 cubic foot consisting of an account book and a letter of a Mercer County judge prominent in civic affairs; *Cemetery Records Collection,* ca. 1.25 cubic feet of records of burials prior to 1900 in ca. 35 Mercer County cemeteries; *Daybook and Ledger Collection* (1800-1935) ; ca. 15 cubic feet of business records and justice of the peace dockets, most of which date from the second half of the 19th C.; *Garvin and Trunkey Papers* (1824-1906), ca. .75 cubic foot of business letters and personal papers, etc., of two prominent Mercer County families, including items of William Swan Garvin, the editor of the *Western Press* and a congressman (1845-47), and John Trunkey, a lawyer and a justice of the Pennsylvania Supreme Court; *Griff W. Nicholls Collection* (1860-1955), ca. 14.30 cubic feet of records kept by Nicholls, a civil engineer who did a great deal of work in Mercer County, the records of his father James Nicholls, a mining engineer turned civil engineer and the James A. Leech Survey Books, which deal with civil work; *Pierce Family Papers* (1851-1863), ca. 1 cubic foot of the business papers of a Mercer County family with interests in coal, iron, canals, and banking; interesting miscellaneous items include the minute book of the Mercer County WCTU (1874-1887) and the minutes of the Jefferson Literary Society (1853-1854); and others.

COPY SERVICES: Photocopying can be arranged.

Milford

PIKE COUNTY HISTORICAL SOCIETY

Community House, Milford.

Curator: Mrs. Ketchum Depuy

Hours: Summer: 2:00-5:00 P. M., Saturday, and by appointment. Address society or Mr. Norman Ledhy, first vice-president.

HOLDINGS: Approximately 1 cubic foot of manuscript and typescript materials neither arranged nor indexed. Included are materials *Cemeteries, Graveyards, and Burying Grounds, in Pike Co., Pennsylvania,* compiled by V. W. Fields, 2 typescript volumes, ca. 10 cubic foot; *Miscellaneous Materials from the Pike County Courthouse* (1800-1904), ca. .70 cubic foot including trial records, court dockets, and election returns; and others.

COPY SERVICES: Photocopies available.

Montrose

SUSQUEHANNA COUNTY HISTORICAL SOCIETY AND FREE LIBRARY ASSOCIATION

Library, Montrose.

Librarian: Mrs. Mabel C. Lyons

Hours: October through May, 1:00-5:00 P. M., Friday. June through September, 1:00-5:00 P. M., Tuesday and Friday; and by appointment.

HOLDINGS: Approximately 5 cubic feet of manuscript materials, partially catalogued and arranged. Included are *Business Records Collection* (early 19th C.-early 20th C.), ca. 2 cubic feet of daybooks, ledgers, etc., of a county carpentry shop, a general store, a carding factory (1830's), a watch repairman, several doctors, etc.; *Church Records* (1819-early 20th C.), lists of members, baptisms, and minutes of 16 county churches; *County Records Collection* (early 19th C.), ca. 1 cubic foot of justice of the peace dockets, tax lists, lists of voters; *Genealogical Material*, ca. 1 cubic foot; interesting miscellanea include Civil War letters, Galusha Grow's will, 2 letters (1879) to Grow offering him the ambassadorship to Russia, and papers relating to the 1903 county celebration of Grow's homecoming; and others.

COPY SERVICES: Limited photocopies available.

Muncy

MUNCY HISTORICAL SOCIETY AND MUSEUM OF HISTORY

North Main Street, Muncy.

Archivist: Mrs. Fred L. Phillips

Hours: By appointment. Address inquiries to E. P. Bertin, President, South Main Street, Muncy.

HOLDINGS: Approximately 1.5 cubic feet of manuscript and typescript materials, partially arranged and catalogued. Included are items such as teachers monthly reports, Point School No. 1, Shrewsbury School District, Lycoming County (1881-1894); miscellaneous ledgers and daybooks; a few deeds; family histories; and others.

COPY SERVICES: No set policy.

Nazareth

THE CHURCH OF THE UNITED BRETHREN OF THE TOWN OF NAZARETH AND ITS VICINITY
(Commonly, the Nazareth Moravian Church)

Nazareth.

Pastor: John S. Goserud

Hours: By appointment.

HOLDINGS: Approximately 40 cubic feet of manuscripts and typescripts neither arranged nor catalogued. Materials include *Diaries of the Nazareth Congregation* (1744-1922), along with translated extracts for the years 1740-1742, 1773-1812; *Translated Diary of Gnadenthal* (1753-1772); *Diary of Christian Spring* (1757-1769); *Reports of North Carolina Congregations* (1788-1810); *Board of Elders Papers* (1770-1802), including a list of members, reports of meetings, and much correspondence from prominent Moravians; and others. Collections are closely related to those at the Moravian Historical Society.

COPY SERVICES: None.

MORAVIAN HISTORICAL SOCIETY

Whitefield House, Nazareth.

Librarian: Rev. Edward Swavely

Hours: By appointment only.

HOLDINGS: Approximately 56 cubic feet of manuscript material which is both unarranged and unsorted. Holdings include the *Barony of Nazareth Material* (1740-1800), ca. 8 cubic feet of manuscripts pertaining to settlements within the "barony" including the farming center of Gnadenthal, the single brethren's vocational training community of the Friedensthal, and a center of some Indian trade, the Rose Inn and Hotel; *Gemein Nachrichten* (1755-1836), ca. 6.7 cubic feet of a collection of biographies, reports, journals, and sermons of the church at large; *Nazareth Hall School* (1755-1929), ca. 34 cubic feet of papers and records of the now defunct boys' school; and others.

COPY SERVICES: None.

SEE: *Transactions of the Moravian Historical Society*

New Castle

NEW CASTLE FREE PUBLIC LIBRARY

106 East North Street, New Castle.

Librarian: Miss Helen Roux

Hours: 10:00 A. M.-9:00 P. M., Monday through Friday; 9:00 A. M.-5:30 P. M., Saturday.

HOLDINGS: Approximately .27 cubic foot of materials, property of the now inactive Lawrence County Historical Society. Included are the *Ira D. Sankey Collection* (1893-1940), ca. .02 cubic foot of letters written by Sankey to his son Fred Sankey; *Robert F. Moffat Collection* (1862-1876), ca. .15 cubic foot, diary, military papers, and widow's pension requests pertaining to a captain in the 100th Regt. of Pa. Volun.; and others.

COPY SERVICES: None.

Norristown

HISTORICAL SOCIETY OF MONTGOMERY COUNTY

1654 De Kalb Street, Norristown.

Librarian: Mrs. LeRoy Burris

Hours: 10:00 A.M.-12:00 M., 1:00-4:00 P. M., Monday through Friday.

HOLDINGS: Approximately 500 cubic feet of manuscript and typescript material, partially arranged and indexed, including *Elijah Brooke Papers* (1837-1858), ca. .50 cubic foot of road petitions and land draughts and attendant calculations pertaining to Chester,

Delaware, and Montgomery counties; *Hiram Corson Papers* (1827-1896), ca. 3 cubic feet of material including an 1827 journal kept while a student at the University of Pennsylvania Medical School, a 15-volume journal-diary (1832-1896), which presents a picture of the "comfortable life" of the latter part of the 19th C., and medical papers and records concerning primarily the treatment of the insane, all accumulated by Dr. Corson, a physician with a lively interest in abolition, who practiced in Montgomery County; *Donnaldson Family Papers*, (1776-1914), material amassed by a Philadelphia-Montgomery County family which produced several sea captains: manuscripts include diary kept on a trip to Niagara Falls in 1824, notes on a trade voyage to China in 1818, documents pertaining to land transactions, personal letters, and business receipts; *Joseph Fornance Collection* (1830-1910), ca. 1.25 cubic feet consisting mainly of routine correspondence sent and received during his years (1839-1843) as a United States representative; *John and Charles Swift Collection* (1747-1821), ca. .75 cubic foot of material comprising business papers of Philadelphia merchants, John and Charles Swift and John Thomas Riche, involved during the 1780's in trade with England; *Montgomery County Tax Assessment Records* (1785-1938), ca. 120 cubic feet of these (1785-1846) are stored and administered in the society's building—the rest (1846-1938) are stored in a nearby garage; *Business Account Books and Records of Local Bridge and Turnpike Companies* (1766-1920), ca. 50 cubic feet; *Deeds* (1730-1865), ca. 36 cubic feet of local deeds, indexed by grantor and grantee; *Charles R. Barker Collection*, ca. 18 cubic feet of genealogical materials pertaining mainly to Lower Merion; other genealogical materials, ca. 42 cubic feet, including transcriptions of church and graveyard records, vital statistics abstracted from local English and German newspapers, and family charts; and others.

COPY SERVICES: None.

Pennsburg

SCHWENKFELDER LIBRARY

Pennsburg.

Director: Andrew S. Berky

Hours: 9:00 A. M.-4:00 P. M., Monday through Friday.

HOLDINGS: Approximately 140 cubic feet of manuscript and typescript materials, mostly arranged and catalogued. The despository contains both Schwenkfelder materials and general materials from the upper Perkiomen Valley. Included are the *Bound Manuscript Collection* (1550-1830), ca. 36 cubic feet consisting of 600 volumes of theological treatises and devotional literature relating to the Schwenkfelders in Silesia and Pennsylvania; *Business Records Collection* (1764-1918), ca. 18 cubic feet of account books and ledgers relating mostly to Schwenkfelders and residents of the upper Perkiomen Valley;

Cipher Books Collection, ca. 4 cubic feet, mostly 19 C. school books; *Deed Collection,* ca. 18 cubic feet consisting of 5,000 items; *Genealogical Records,* ca. 5.5 cubic feet; *Landis Collection,* ca. 7.5 cubic feet of materials devoted to the genealogy of the Landis and allied families; there are also ca. 50 cubic feet of miscellaneous materials relating to Schwenkfelder life in Pennsylvania (c. 1700-1900).

COPY SERVICES: Microfilming and photocopying can be arranged.

Philadelphia

ACADEMY OF NATURAL SCIENCES OF PHILADELPHIA

Library, 19th and the Parkway, Philadelphia.

Manuscript Librarian: Mrs. Venia T. Phillips

Hours: 9:00 A. M.-5:00 P. M., Monday through Friday.

HOLDINGS: Approximately 355 cubic feet of manuscript and type-script material, mostly arranged and catalogued, deals principally with the history of the natural sciences in America. The more important collections include the *Lewis David von Schweinitz Papers* (1802-1833), the *Homer Franklin Bassett Papers* (1864-1901), the *Zaccheus Collins Papers* (1805-1827), the *Samuel Stehman Haldeman Papers* (1830-1880), the *Joseph Leidy Papers* (1840-1910), the *Thomas and Lucy Say Papers* (1812-1885), the *Charles Eastwick Smith Papers* (1867-1899), and others.

COPY SERVICES: Limited photocopying. Microfilm available for larger orders.

SEE: Venia T. and Maurice E. Phillips, *Guide to the Manuscript Collections of the Academy of Natural Sciences,* Special Publication No. 5, Philadelphia: The Academy, 1963.

AMERICAN PHILOSOPHICAL SOCIETY

Library, 105 South Fifth Street, Philadelphia.

Manuscript Librarian: Murphy D. Smith

Hours: 9:00 A. M.-5:00 P. M., Monday through Friday.

HOLDINGS: Its approximately 1,264 cubic feet of manuscript and typescript materials, which emphasizes the history of science, comprises one of the most significant manuscript collections in Pennsylvania. Among the society's most important holdings, in addition to its own archives, are the *Benjamin Franklin Papers,* the *Franz Boas Collection of American Indian Linguistics, Charles Willson Peale Family Papers,* and the *Lewis and Clark Journals.*

COPY SERVICES: Microfilm and photocopies.

SEE: John F. Freeman, *A Guide to the Manuscripts Relating to the American Indian in the Library of the American Philosophical Society,*

Philadelphia: The Society, 1965; scheduled for publication in 1965 is a guide to the general collections of the society being prepared by Murphy Smith and Whitfield Bell.

AMERICAN SWEDISH HISTORICAL MUSEUM

1900 Pattison Avenue, Philadelphia.

Director: John H. Wilkens

Hours: 10:00 A. M.-5:00 P. M., Monday through Friday; 1:00-5:00 P. M., Saturday. Make an appointment in writing prior to a visit.

HOLDINGS: Approximately 20,000 items, partially arranged and catalogued, which relate chiefly to early Swedish settlers in America. Also included are a quantity of the papers of *John Ericsson,* the American-Swedish engineer, inventor, and designer of the "Monitor" and other naval vessels; and papers and letters from and relating to *Jenny Lind,* the "Swedish Nightingale"; and others.

COPY SERVICES: No set policy.

CHRIST CHURCH

20 North American Street, Philadelphia.

Rector: Rev. Dr. Ernest A. Harding

Hours: By appointment only.

HOLDINGS: Approximately 1.25 cubic feet of manuscript material plus the usual church records. Included in the collection are ca. 1 cubic foot of *Sermons of Bishop White;* a George Washington letter; a few deeds; and others.

COPY SERVICES: Photocopying can be arranged.

THE COLLEGE OF PHYSICIANS OF PHILADELPHIA

19 South Twenty-Second Street, Philadelphia.

Curator of Library's Historical Collections: Dr. W. B. McDaniel, 2nd

Hours: Winter months: 9:00 A. M.-9:30 P. M., Monday and Wednesday; 9:00 A. M.-5:00 P. M., Tuesday, Thursday, Friday, and Saturday; Summer months: 1:00-9:30 P. M., Tuesday; 9:00 A. M.-5:00 P. M., Monday, Wednesday, Thursday, and Friday.

HOLDINGS: Approximately 462 cubic feet of manuscript and typescript materials pertaining to medicine, medical institutions, and medical men, especially, but not exclusively, of the Philadelphia area. Most materials are arranged and catalogued individually. There are two major collections, *Gilbert Collection* (1729-1842), ca. 1.5 cubic feet of autograph letters contained in four volumes—included are letters of or to John Bartram, Aaron Burr, Benjamin Chew, John

31

Redman Coxe, and Israel Pemberton; and *Medical School Notes Collection* (1746-1885), 153 sets of notes for lectures and notes taken by medical students both in America and in Edinburgh: collection includes notes pertaining to David Hosack, Nathaniel Chapman, Benjamin S. Barton, Adam Kuhn, John K. and S. Weir Mitchell, Benjamin Rush, and Caspar Wistar.

COPY SERVICES: Photocopies.

SEE: "Fugitive Leaves," second series, mimeographed looseleaf leaflets issued by the college, January, 1956, to the present.

DEPARTMENT OF RECORDS OF PHILADELPHIA YEARLY MEETING OF THE RELIGIOUS SOCIETY OF FRIENDS

302 Arch Street, Philadelphia.

Secretary: Miss Mary Ogilvie

Hours: 9:00 A. M.-5:00 P. M., Monday through Friday.

HOLDINGS: Approximately 791 cubic feet of manuscript records, both arranged and catalogued, on deposit from the various meetings, both active and inactive (1681-present).

COPY SERVICES: Photocopying and microfilming can be arranged.

THE FRANKLIN INSTITUTE

20th and the Parkway, Philadelphia.

Director of Libraries: Dr. John McGowan

Hours: Winter: 9:00 A. M.-5:00 P. M., Monday, Tuesday, Friday, and Saturday; 2:00-10:00 P. M., Wednesday; 9:00 A. M.-10:00 P. M. Thursday. Summer: 9:00 A. M.-5:00 P. M., Monday, Wednesday, Thursday, and Friday; 9:00 A. M.-10:00 P. M., Tuesday; 9:00 A.M.-12:00 M., Saturday. It is wise to make an appointment

HOLDINGS: Manuscript and typescript materials partially arranged and indexed which deal with scientific and technological history. Included in the library are the *Daybook of Richard Bache,* which contains entries of transactions made on behalf of Benjamin Franklin (1772-1792); *Samuel Vaughan, Jr., Manuscripts* (1772-1782), the notebooks and letters of an Anglo-American who had strong interest in science; *Oliver Evans Papers* (1800-1814), mostly legal papers pertaining to litigations concerning his patent flour mill; *Wright Brothers Aeronautical Engineering Collection* (1903-1910), drawings and manuscripts dealing with the birth of powered flight; *John Lenthall Collection* (c. 1776-1874), the papers of Lenthall and his collection which deal with the construction of naval vessels; *Oliver Wolcott Gibbs Papers* (1847-1908), ca. 1,500 items, mostly scientific correspondence of a Harvard chemistry professor; interesting miscellanea include an autograph album containing the signatures of the delegates to and officers of the Pennsylvania Constitutional Convention of 1837-1838, and the log of the whaler "Franklin" (1833-1837) out of Sag Harbor, N. Y.; and others. The most interesting item in the institute's museum is Franklin's 1757 will.

COPY SERVICES: Photocopies and microfilm.

SEE: *Pennsylvania Magazine of History and Biography,* LXXX (Jan. 1956), 46-49; *Journal of the Franklin Institute,* CCXLVII (Mar. 1949), 195-204, CCLII (Aug. 1951), 175-196.

FREE LIBRARY OF PHILADELPHIA

Rare Book Department, Logan Square, Philadelphia.

Rare Book Librarian: Miss Ellen Shaffer

Hours: 9:00 A. M.-5:30 P. M., Monday through Friday; 9:00 A. M.-5:00 P. M., Saturday.

HOLDINGS: Approximately 33 cubic feet of manuscript and type-script materials, largely arranged and catalogued. Included are *Hampton L. Carson Collection* (1565-1922), ca. 24 cubic feet consisting of ca. 3,400 American and English autographs, including letters of each justice of the U. S. Supreme Court from Jay to Brandeis; *Ephrata Cloister Collection* (1786-1894), ca. .15 cubic foot consisting of ca. 500 small items, mostly bills and receipts, but also containing appraisals of personal effects, etc.; *William McIntire Elkins Collection* (1781-1828), ca. .30 cubic foot consisting of 100 items dealing with Anglo-American relations, including documents on the negotiation of Jay's Treaty, and individual documents by John Adams, John Jay, Alexander Hamilton, Thomas Jefferson, John Marshall, Benjamin Rush, George Washington, and others; *Minutes of the Common Council of Philadelphia* (Oct. 1704-Feb. 1776), ca. .75 cubic foot consisting of 300 papers contained in six volumes; *L. Stauffer Oliver Papers* (1945-1948), ca. 7.5 cubic feet of correspondence, minutes, etc., of a committee with which Oliver was extremely active, to have Philadelphia chosen as the headquarters for the United Nations; *Norman H. and Charlotte Strouse Collection of Presidential Letters,* ca. .40 cubic foot consisting of 60 letters, Washington through Eisenhower; and others.

COPY SERVICES: Positive microfilm and photocopies.

SEE: *Catalog of the Hampton L. Carson Collection Illustrative of the Growth of Common Law in the Free Library of Philadelphia,* 2 vols., Boston: G. K. Hall & Co., 1962.

GERMANTOWN HISTORICAL SOCIETY

5208 Germantown Avenue, Philadelphia.

Secretary: Capt. Edmund A. Crenshaw, Jr.

Hours: 1:00-5:00 P. M., Tuesday. Address inquiries to the Librarian at the society's building.

HOLDINGS: Approximately 7.5 cubic feet of manuscript and typescript materials partially arranged and catalogued. Included are *Business*

Records Collection, ca. 3 cubic feet of the ledgers, account books, and letters of Germantown business organizations; *Deeds and Wills Collection,* ca. 1.5 cubic feet of materials largely from the Germantown area; *Biographical and Genealogical Collection,* ca. 3 cubic feet of files in which manuscript materials are mixed with other matter pertaining to Germantown families; interesting miscellaneous items include a legal bond drawn and signed by Francis Daniel Pastorius, and others.

COPY SERVICES: Photocopying and microfilming can be arranged.

GIRARD COLLEGE

Corinthian and Girard Avenues, Philadelphia.

Librarian: Miss Margaret E. McFate

Hours: By appointment only. Direct inquiries to Dr. Karl R. Friedmann, president.

HOLDINGS: Approximately 668 cubic feet of manuscripts, partially arranged and catalogued, consisting almost entirely of the *Stephen Girard Collection* (1780-1831), which includes both his business and his professional papers; interesting miscellaneous items include the notebook William Strickland kept during the construction of Founder's Hall (1837-1844) and the four other original buildings; and others.

COPY SERVICES: None.

GLORIA DEI (OLD SWEDES') CHURCH

916 South Swanson Street, Philadelphia.

Rector: Rev. John C. Roak, D. D.

Hours: By appointment.

HOLDINGS: Besides church records, there is approximately 1 cubic foot of 18th and 19th C. deeds which are neither arranged nor catalogued.

COPY SERVICES: Photocopying can be arranged.

HISTORICAL SOCIETY OF PENNSYLVANIA

1300 Locust Street, Philadelphia.

Head of Manuscripts Department: J. Harcourt Givens

Hours: 1:00-9:00 P. M., Monday; 9:00 A. M.-5:00 P. M., Tuesday through Friday. Closed during August.

HOLDINGS: This is the largest manuscript depository in Pennsylvania, and one of the most important in the United States. Among its most valuable collections are the *Penn Papers,* the *Cadwalader Collection,* and the *Gratz Autograph Collection*. A truly unique item is the first draft of the United States Constitution which is in the society's possession.

COPY SERVICES: Photocopies and microfilm.

SEE: *Guide to the Manuscript Collections of the Historical Society of Pennsylvania*, Philadelphia: The Society, 1949.

HISTORICAL SOCIETY OF THE PHILADELPHIA METHODIST CONFERENCE

Old St. Georges Methodist Church, 235 North Fourth Street, Philadelphia.

Curator: Dr. Frederick E. Maser

Hours: By appointment.

HOLDINGS: Approximately 130 cubic feet of manuscript materials neither arranged nor catalogued. Included are the *Church Records Collection* (1774-1936), ca. 124 cubic feet of records of defunct Methodist churches in the area of the Philadelphia Conference; *Reverend Joseph Pilmoor Journal* (1769-1773), ca. .25 cubic foot, the journal of St. Georges' first pastor, who later became a pastor in the Episcopal Church; *Journals of the Philadelphia Methodist Conference* (1800-1900), ca. 1.75 cubic feet of materials which are analogous to minutes—supplementing these are the *Papers of the Philadelphia Methodist Conference* (1804-1928), ca. 2.5 cubic feet of trial records, requests for membership, etc.; *Minutes of the Philadelphia Preachers Meetings* (1841-1942), ca. .50 cubic foot; *Minutes of the Philadelphia Foreign Missionary Society* (1883-1932), ca. .75 cubic foot; *Bishop Matthew Simpson Papers* (1872-1882), ca. 1 cubic foot composed mostly of incoming correspondence; letters by John Wesley (5), Francis Asbury (12), George Whitefield (1), Mary Thorn (12), and Thomas Coke (12); and others.

COPY SERVICES: None.

INDEPENDENCE NATIONAL HISTORICAL PARK

420 Chestnut Street, Philadelphia.

Supervisory Museum Curator: Dr. David H. Wallace

Hours: 9:00 A. M.-5:00 P. M., Monday through Friday, except holidays.

HOLDINGS: Approximately 75 cubic feet of manuscript and typescript materials, almost entirely arranged and partially catalogued. Included are *Mrs. Samuel B. Chew Papers* (c. 1873-1917), ca. 3.5 cubic feet of materials on loan to Independence National Historical Park, and which concern her work in behalf of the Independence Hall National Museum; *Ellen Waln Harrison Collection* (1895-1900), ca. 1 cubic foot of papers about the restoration of Independence Hall; *Records of the Board to Take Charge of and Collect Historical Relics for the Museum of Independence Hall* (1900-1917), ca. 1 cubic foot; *Records of the Independence Hall Association* (1943-1960), ca. 10 cubic feet of materials of the organization which began the campaign for the modern restoration of Independence Hall and the development of Independence National Historical Park; *Records of the Independence Hall Division, Bureau of City Property, City of Philadelphia* (c. 1898-1950), ca. 30 cubic feet of materials on loan from the city; *Documents Relating to Restoration of Independence Hall* (1897-1914), ca. 1 cubic foot; *Horace Wells Sellers Collection* (c. 1910-c. 1920), ca. 3.5 cubic feet of materials relating to the restoration of Congress Hall; *Papers Relating to the Second Bank of the United States* (c. 1812-1836), ca. 150 pieces including letters of Nicholas Biddle and others which concern the establishment and operation of the bank, and a retained copy of the petition for recharter; interesting miscellanea include items relating to and by members of the Continental Congress, the Federal Constitutional Convention, officers (including foreign) of the American Revolution, and members of early federal Congresses (1789-1820) — especially important are Jasper Yeates' notes of the debates in the Pennsylvania Ratification Convention (November-December, 1787); and others.

COPY SERVICES: Photocopying and microfilming can be arranged.

LIBRARY COMPANY OF PHILADELPHIA

Broad and Christian Streets, Philadelphia.

Director: Edwin Wolf, 2nd

Hours: 9:00 A. M.-5:00 P. M., Monday through Friday, except legal holidays.

HOLDINGS: Approximately 342 cubic feet of manuscript material, partially arranged and catalogued. Included are *Samuel Breck and Samuel Breck, Jr., Papers* (1748-1797, 1770-1845), ca. 1 cubic foot of materials of the elder Breck, a wealthy merchant of Boston and Philadelphia and a director of the First Bank of the United States, and of his son, State senator and State representative in Pennsylvania—correspondents include Alexander Hamilton, John Paul Jones, Rembrandt Peale, etc.; *Mathew Carey Papers* (1823-1829), 183 items combined in with 40 cubic feet of newspaper clippings, etc.; *John Dickinson Papers* (1754-1808), ca. 6 cubic feet of correspondence, leases, receipts, and papers relating to land and farms in New Jersey and Delaware, etc., includes letters written home while a student at Inns of Court in London—correspondents include Tench Coxe, William and Charles Lee, Caesar Rodney, and Benjamin Rush; *William Dillwyn and Susanna Emlen Correspondence* (?-1824), ca. 1 cubic foot of letters between a father living in London and his daughter living in Burlington, N. J., and Philadelphia: contains comments on social life and customs: *Pierre Eugène Du Simitière Collection* (1736-1784), ca. 2 cubic feet of papers relating to natural history, Indian life, and various aspects of colonial history, particularly of New England, New York, and Pennsylvania; *Stephen Grellet Papers* (1773-1855), ca. 1 cubic foot of correspondence, notes on family history, summaries of sermons of a Quaker minister and missionary; *James Barton Longacre Papers* (1794-1869), ca. 2 cubic feet of incoming correspondence, notebooks, diaries, etc., of a Philadelphia engraver and numismatist whose correspondents included Nicholas Biddle, J. C. Calhoun, Lewis Cass, George Catlin, Asher B. Durand, Edward Everett, S. C. Haynes, James Madison, John Neagle, Joel Poinsett, Thomas and Richard Sully, Daniel Webster, and William Wirt; *John McAllister Collection* (1683-1881), ca. 15,000 items which include records of business firms and Civil War materials; *Morton Family Papers* (1832-1863), ca. 2 cubic feet of papers of Dr. Samuel George Morton, physician and naturalist, who maintained a scientific correspondence, with letters on scientific subjects with Asa Grey, S. S. Haldeman, etc., and of his son General James St. Clair Morton, which relate to the Chiriqui Surveying Expedition, the Civil War, West Point, etc.; *Powel Family Papers* (1723-1853), ca. 8 cubic feet of business papers of the descendants of Samuel Powel (1673-1756) of Philadelphia, including his grandson Samuel Powel, mayor of Philadelphia, and John Hare Powel (1786-1856), author, State senator, soldier, and agriculturist—also included are accounts of the William Bingham estate; *Read Family Papers* (1769-1896), ca. 55 cubic feet of letters and notes of the Read and such related families as the Cadwalader, Howell, and Ross—especially important are papers of John Read, Jr. (1769-1854), president of the Bank of Philadelphia, John Meredith Read, I (1797-1874), chief justice of Pennsylvania, and John Meredith Read, II (1837-1896), lawyer, diplomat, and historical scholar; *Benjamin Rush Papers* (1762-1813), ca. 17 cubic feet of correspondence, medical writings, notebooks of various phases of the physician's many activities; *James Rush Papers* (1802-1869), ca. 12 cubic feet of correspondence, etc., of a pioneer in the study of the human voice; *John Jay Smith Collection* (1678-1883), ca. 8 cubic feet including personal correspondence of Smith, a librarian of the Library Company of Philadelphia, and an extensive correspondence between William Logan and Smith's grandfather, John Smith; *Thomas Truxton Letters* (1787-1820), 110 letters, all but 3 of which are written to Charles Biddle, concerning Truxton's naval, business, and domestic affairs, and containing instructions to Biddle, who acted as Truxton's agent in the disposal of prize monies, etc., together with references to Jefferson and the Burr Affair, etc.; *Union Fire Company Records* (1736-1843), 5 volumes of minutes and articles of association of a Philadelphia fire company; *Waln Family Papers* (1784-c. 1823), 25 volumes of letter books of Robert and Jesse Waln, Philadelphia merchants and insurance brokers, and papers of Robert Waln, Jr., relating to the China trade, etc.; and others.

COPY SERVICES: Photocopying and microfilming can be arranged.

THE WAR LIBRARY AND MUSEUM OF THE MILITARY ORDER OF THE LOYAL LEGION OF THE UNITED STATES

1805 Pine Street, Philadelphia.

Secretary of the Library: J. Truman Swing

Hours: 10:00 A. M.-4:30 P. M., Monday through Saturday.

HOLDINGS: Approximately 1 cubic foot of manuscript and typescript materials, catalogued but not arranged. Included are the *Louis R. Fortescue Diary* (1861-1865), ca. .50 cubic foot consisting of a 5-volume typescript prepared at a later period from original notes and interleaved with memorabilia and manuscript letters; *William Brook Rawle Letters* (1863-1865), ca. .10 cubic foot written by a lieutenant, later a captain of the Third Pennsylvania Cavalry, from Virginia, mostly to his mother; *Thomas Skelton Harrison Diary* (1897-1899), ca. .10 cubic foot consisting of 3 volumes kept by Harrison when he served as United States ambassador to Egypt; *Records of Official Orders Received by James W. King* (1844-1881), ca. .10 cubic foot of materials amassed by a chief engineer who served on several naval vessels; *George R. Snowden Diary* (1862), ca. .10 cubic foot pertaining to the career of a soldier from Franklin, Pennsylvania; interesting miscellaneous items include a Mary Todd Lincoln letter and a William T. Sherman letter; and others.

COPY SERVICES: None.

THE LUTHERAN THEOLOGICAL SEMINARY

Krauth Memorial Library, 7301 Germantown Avenue, Philadelphia.

Librarian: Dr. Henry Scherer

Hours: Academic year: 8:45 A. M.-5:00 P. M., 7:00-10:00 P. M., Monday through Thursday; 8:45 A. M.-5:00 P. M., Friday; 9:00 A. M.-12:00 M., Saturday. Vacations: 9:00 A. M.-5:00 P. M., Monday through Friday; 9:00 A. M.-12:00 M., Saturday.

HOLDINGS: Approximately 368 cubic feet of manuscript and typescript materials, largely arranged and catalogued. The school is the official depository of the Eastern Pennsylvania Synod of the Lutheran Church in America and as such it houses the *Records of General Council of the Evangelical Lutheran Church of North America* (1868-1921), ca. 16 cubic feet including correspondence, minutes of conventions, minutes and reports relating to foreign and home missions, records of the National Lutheran Commission for Soldiers and Sailors' Welfare, the original draft of the Galesburg Rule (1875), etc., and a large number or records of defunct churches. Other holdings include *Justus Christian Henry Helmuth Papers* (1767-1821), ca. 5 cubic feet of correspondence, a 90-volume diary (1767-1810), sermon notes, church records, account books, and a fragmentary autobiography of a Lutheran pastor, author, and professor; *Paul and Socrates Henkel Collection* (1754-1894), ca. 2 cubic feet of the papers of two Lutheran ministers, grandfather Paul and grandson Socrates—Paul, a pastor in New Market, Virginia, kept a diary and wrote a 3-volume account of his 1806 missionary journeys to Ohio and North Carolina; *Michael Jacobs Papers* (c. 1828-1865), ca. .50 cubic foot of correspondence, lecture notes, church records of a Lutheran pastor and educator—included in the collection are papers from Jefferson College, Canonsburg, Pennsylvania (c. 1828-1847); *Beale Melanchton Schmucker Papers* (1848-1888), ca. 2 cubic feet of correspondence and historical writings concerning the Lutheran Church in America; *Henry Melchior Muhlenberg Papers* (1733-1787), ca. 4 cubic feet of correspondence, sermon notes, reports, and a 26-volume diary kept by this prominent Lutheran patriot; and others.

COPY SERVICES: Photocopying can be arranged.

SEE: W. H. Allison, *Inventory of Unpublished Material for American Religious History in Protestant Church Archives and Other Repositories,* Washington, 1910.

CONGREGATION MIKVEH ISRAEL

Broad and York Streets, Philadelphia.

President: Philip I. Margolis

Hours: By appointment. Address correspondence to the President, 6701 North Broad Street, Philadelphia.

HOLDINGS: In addition to significant institutional records, holdings include a number of interesting and unique items of American Judaica. Included are George Washington's letter to the Hebrew Congregations of Philadelphia, New York, Charleston, and Richmond; Jacob Raphael Cohen's home book, in Hebrew (1809); personal record book (1776-1843) in Hebrew and English kept by Dr. A. I. Weirtheim, the congregation's second minister; records of circumcisions kept in Dutch by Barnard Jacobs (1760), *mahel* of Heidelberg, Pennsylvania; and miscellaneous 18th C. deeds of members of the Jewish community; etc.

COPY SERVICES: None.

PHILADELPHIA HISTORICAL COMMISSION

Room 634, City Hall, Philadelphia.

Historian: Dr. Margaret B. Tinkcom

Hours: 9:00 A. M.-5:00 P. M., Monday through Friday. It is, however, advisable to make an appointment.

HOLDINGS: In addition to a notable collection of graphic materials, there are approximately 45 cubic feet of manuscript and typescript materials, arranged and catalogued. Most of the collection consists of histories of individual Philadelphia buildings gathered from official records and the files of insurance companies. Materials are arranged by street and number.

COPY SERVICES: None.

PHILADELPHIA MARITIME MUSEUM

219 South Sixth Street, Philadelphia.

Director: John W. Jackson

Hours: 10:00 A. M.-4:00 P. M., Monday through Saturday; 1:00-5:00 P. M., Sunday. Make an appointment before a visit.

HOLDINGS: Approximately 3 cubic feet of manuscript and typescript material, not arranged or catalogued. Included are *Cramp Ship Building Company Records* (1878-1922), ca. .40 cubic foot, two volumes which contain records of ships built, their cost, purchasers, etc.; some David Farragut letters; and others. This is a young organization and work is going on.

COPY SERVICES: Photocopying can be arranged.

PRESBYTERIAN HISTORICAL SOCIETY

520 Witherspoon Building, Philadelphia.

Librarian: William B. Miller

Hours: 9:00 A. M.-5:00 P. M., Monday through Friday, except legal holidays.

HOLDINGS: Approximately 825 cubic feet of manuscript and typescript materials, mostly arranged and indexed, pertaining to the Presbyterian church and individual Presbyterians. Materials include *American Indian Missionary Correspondence* (1832-1893), ca. 14 cubic feet of letters written by Presbyterian missionaries; *John D. Shane Collection* (1716-1860), ca. 9 cubic feet of documents relating to Presbyterian institutions especially of Tennessee, Ohio, Indiana, Kentucky, and Illinois—including source materials on the early history of Transylvania University; *Domestic Mission Letters* (1831-1900), ca. 36 cubic feet consisting of some 50,000 letters of the Western Foreign Missionary Society and the Presbyterian Board of Foreign Missions concerning work done in the United States; *Correspondence of the Board of Aid for Colleges* (1884-1918), ca. 4 cubic feet of letters concerning the financial support given to some 50 Presbyterian-affiliated schools in America; *Records of Synods and Presbyteries,* ca. 233 cubic feet; *Records of Individual Churches,* ca. 333 cubic feet; *Sheldon Jackson Collection* (1856-1908), ca. 11 cubic feet of letters relating to newly established churches in the Rocky Mountain area, and to religious, educational, and food problems in Alaska amassed by an early minister there, who served as the territory's U. S. superintendent of education and who is credited with introducing reindeer from Siberia to meet the food problem of native Alaskans; *Records of Boards and Agencies of the Church,* ca. 97 cubic feet; *Sermons Collection,* ca. 26.5 cubic feet of works by many outstanding ministers from the colonial period to the present including some by William Tennent, Samuel Davies, John Rogers, Henry Van Dyke, and John Witherspoon; and others.

COPY SERVICES: Photocopies and microfilm.

SEE: "Index of American Indian Correspondence," *Journal of the Presbyterian Historical Society, XXXI* (March, 1953); and the pamphlet, *Special Collections in the Presbyterian Historical Society,* available from the society.

ST. PETER'S CHURCH IN THE CITY OF PHILADELPHIA

Third and Pine Streets, Philadelphia.

Rector: Rev. Joseph Koci, Jr.

Hours: By appointment. Direct inquiries to the office, St. Peter's Church, 319 Lombard Street.

HOLDINGS: In addition to parish records (1758-present) there is about .25 cubic foot of manuscript material now in process of arrangement, including letters of Jacob Duché, Bishop White, and Stephen Decatur.

COPY SERVICES: None.

UNIVERSITY OF PENNSYLVANIA

Patterson Van Pelt Library, Philadelphia.

Curator, Rare Book Collections: Mrs. Neda M. Westlake

Hours: 9:00 A. M.-5:00 P. M., Monday through Friday; 9:00 A. M.-1:00 P. M., Saturday. Address correspondence to above or to Mr. Lyman Riley, bibliographer.

HOLDINGS: Approximately 18,000 cubic feet of manuscript and typescript materials, mostly arranged and catalogued. A large proportion of the material relates to Pennsylvania and American history, science, and literature. Historical documents housed in the Rare Book Collections include *Thomas H. Burrowes Papers* (1836-1839), 2 letter books of an advocate of a public school system; *George M. Dallas Papers* (1837-1839, 1856-1860), 2 vols. of materials of a U. S. diplomat and vice-president; *Benjamin Franklin Papers* (1777-1778), 11 vols.; *Samuel Delucenna Papers* (1820-1860), ca. 5.5 cubic feet of incoming correspondence from governmental figures and 2 letter books of a man (1779-1860) who was a member of the House of Representatives from Pennsylvania and Andrew Jackson's first secretary of state—resigning to protest Jackson's handling of the Peggy Eaton affair, and who spent the rest of his life developing Pennsylvania's anthracite coal fields; *James Monroe Papers* (1817-1835), 29 items which include several letters addressed to John Quincy Adams; *Francis Daniel Pastorius Papers*

(1696-1719), 2 vols. of materials pertaining to the founder of German-town; *Dr. William Pepper Papers* (1876-1900), 12 vols. of materials of a Pennsylvania physician and educator; *Samuel Jackson Randall Papers* (1844-1890), ca. 135 cubic feet amassed by a Pennsylvania Civil War officer and politician; interesting miscellanea include items by Nicholas Biddle, James Buchanan, John C. Calhoun, John Jay, and Thomas Jefferson; and others. The *Edgar Fahs Smith Memorial Collection,* housed in separate quarters, is best known for its collection of manuscripts of famous chemists, but it also houses letters by a number of men prominent in American history, including George Clymer, Benjamin Franklin, Francis Hopkinson, Robert Morris, William Paca, John Penn, Benjamin Rush, Anthony Wayne, and Benjamin West.

COPY SERVICES: Photocopies available.

Pittsburgh

CARNEGIE LIBRARY OF PITTSBURGH

4400 Forbes Avenue, Pittsburgh.

Head, Pennsylvania Division: Miss H. Dorothy English

Hours: 9:00 A. M.-6:00 P. M., Monday through Friday; 9:00 A. M.-6:00 P. M., Saturday, by appointment; 2:00-5:00 P. M., Sunday, by appointment.

HOLDINGS: Approximately 21.6 cubic feet of manuscript materials both arranged and catalogued. Included are the *Craig Collection* (1766-1850), ca. 14 cubic feet consisting of approximately 12,000 items, most of which are account books, memoranda, correspondence, quarter-master and ordnance records, etc., dated mostly from 1791 through 1801 when Isaac Craig was an officer in the Western Army—his son Henry Knox Craig was later in charge of Watertown and Harper's Ferry arsenals; *George Morgan Letter Books* (1775-1779), ca. .10 cubic foot, 3 vols., dealing with his career as an Indian agent; *Harmar Denny Papers* (1829-1834), ca. .50 cubic foot of materials dealing mostly with land in the Ligonier Valley; *John Neville Papers* (1794-1800), ca. .10 cubic foot, 133 items, correspondence and lists submitted to the collector of internal revenue giving specific locations of stills in Western Pennsylvania; *Miscellaneous Pennsylvania Manuscripts Collection,* ca. 7 cubic feet, largely 19th C. materials including correspondence, Civil War papers, Pittsburgh borough and city records (1792-1859), business records, organizational records, church documents, etc.; interesting miscellanea include the George Croghan journal (1765), which contains one of five known contemporary MS copies of the treaty of Pittsburgh; and others.

COPY SERVICES: Photocopies.

DARLINGTON MEMORIAL LIBRARY

University of Pittsburgh, Pittsburgh.

Darlington Librarian: Miss Ruth Salisbury

Hours: 9:00 A. M.-12:00 M., 1:00-5:00 P. M., Monday through Friday.

HOLDINGS: Approximately 58 cubic feet of manuscript and typescript material, largely catalogued and arranged. Included are *Alexander Addison Papers* (1786-1803), ca. .20 cubic foot includes letters from Charles Nisbet to Addison (1786-1803), some of which discuss the ratification of the Constitution, letters from William Findley (1791-1796) which also discuss ratification, and letters from Hugh Henry Brackenridge to Addison (1790-1798), some of which discuss Jay's Treaty; *Beazel Papers* (1809-1896), ca. .50 cubic foot of business papers dealing with land transactions in Westmoreland County; *Darlington Colonial and Early Republic Collection* (1680-c. 1830), ca. 13.80 cubic feet includes letters of William Pitt, James Wilkinson, Benjamin Franklin, George Washington, Henry Bouquet, and John Forbes, etc.; *Darlington Miscellaneous Collection* (1790-1948), ca. 1.5 cubic feet of autograph letters of statesmen, generals, and writers; *Fort Pitt Manuscripts* (1758-1783), 34 letters and documents relating to the defense and mainenance of the fort; *James P. Leaf Papers* (1891-1940), ca. 15.75 cubic feet of blue prints, specifications, professional, and personal correspondence of a prominent Western Pennsylvania civil engineer who worked for municipalities and was interested in the Erie and Ohio River Canal; *Dunning McNair Papers* (1786-1851), ca. 1 cubic foot of papers of Dunning McNair and his son Dunning Robert McNair which deal with land speculation and development in northwest Pennsylvania, including materials relating to the Pennsylvania Population Company and information on stage lines and mail contracts; *Joseph Leger d'Happart Papers* (1797-1815), ca. 6 cubic feet of business papers which discuss economic conditions in France and America, amassed by a Frenchman who settled first in Connellsville and then in Somerset; *Martin Papers* (1893-1898), ca. 1 cubic foot of business papers of the paint and varnish firm of Martin and McCullough, and manuscripts relating to the labor organization activities of William Martin; *Ohio Company Papers* (1717-1821), ca. .70 cubic foot includes correspondence of George and John Mercer and George Mason; *Schenley-Croghan Papers,* 17 letters to William Croghan from his attorney, daughter, and others after the elopement of Mary with Captain Schenley in 1842, and 25 letters relating to William Croghan's land dealings and other business and political matters (1797-1831); *Taylor-Mackey Papers* (1842-c. 1910), ca. 6 cubic feet of business papers of a Franklin legal firm which worked in oil and represented the Allegheny Valley Railroad; *Thaddeus S. Sheldon Papers* (1853-1865), ca. 2.1 cubic feet of papers, letters, minutes, and financial records of the Kiantone Harmonia, a utopian community established on the New York-Pennsylvania boundary, partly in Chautauqua County, New York; interesting miscellanea include a letter book of Robert J. Walker (1833-1848), U. S. senator with a special interest in Latin America, and a ledger containing the records of the Northern Liberties Bridge Company (1836-1910); and others.

COPY SERVICES: Photocopying and microfilming can be arranged.

See: Ruth Salisbury, "Survey of the Darlington Library," *Western Pennsylvania Historical Magazine*, XLVIII (Jan. 1964), 19-29; Agnes Starrett, *The Darlington Memorial Library, University of Pittsburgh*, Pittsburgh: University of Pittsburgh Press, 1938.

HISTORICAL SOCIETY OF WESTERN PENNSYLVANIA

4338 Bigelow Boulevard, Pittsburgh.

Librarian-Editor: Miss Prudence B. Trimble

Hours: 10:00 A. M.-4:30 P. M., Tuesday through Friday; 10:00 A. M.-12:00 M., Saturday. Closed holidays and August.

HOLDINGS: Approximately 126 cubic feet of manuscript and typescript materials, partially arranged and indexed, which are being rearranged according to a new system. Included are the *John and William Thaw Papers* (1802-1917), ca. 5.5 cubic feet dealing mostly with Pittsburgh business; *William J. Holland Papers* (c. 1874-c. 1932), ca. 33 cubic feet amassed by a scientist who was later chancellor of the University of Pittsburgh and a director of the Carnegie Art Museum; *Col. Jacob D. Mathiot Collection* (1811-1877), ca. 18.5 cubic feet of largely business correspondence and records dealing with land transactions and the iron industry in the Ligonier Valley; *Society Miscellaneous Collection* (1701-present), ca. 8.5 cubic feet arranged in chronological order; *Robert McKnight Diaries* (1840's), .30 cubic foot kept by a prominent Pittsburgh attorney; *Common and Select Council Records, City of Pittsburgh* (1805-c. 1850), ca. 6 cubic feet; *Turner Fricke Manufacturing Company Records* (1920-1924), ca. 3.5 cubic feet; *Business Ledgers Collection*, ca. 12 cubic feet; *Isaac and Neville Craig Papers* (1775-1859), ca. 1.3 cubic feet—Isaac was a military officer who served in Western Pennsylvania; *Butler, Westmoreland, and Greene County Tax Records* (1800-1847 broken runs), ca. 6 cubic feet; *Denny-O'Hara Papers* (1796-1832), ca. 6.5 cubic feet dealing with military and business affairs in Western Pennsylvania—includes papers of Gen. James O'Hara, Congressman Harmar Denny, and Maj. Ebenezer Denny; *John Covode Papers* (1850's), ca. 1.5 cubic feet dealing with the career of a congressman from Westmoreland County; *John Harper Papers* (1839-1882), ca. 3 cubic feet dealing with a prominent Pittsburgh family; *Spring Chalfant and Company Papers* (1850's), ca. .50 cubic foot of materials dealing with iron manufacture; interesting miscellanea include Fort Pitt daybooks (1765-1767, 1772); and others.

COPY SERVICES: Photocopying and microfilming can be arranged.

PITTSBURGH THEOLOGICAL SEMINARY

616 North Highland Avenue, Pittsburgh.

Librarian: Dr. James Irvine

Hours: Academic year: 7:50 A. M.-5:30 P. M., 7:00-10:30 P. M., Monday through Friday; 9:30 A. M.-3:30 P. M., Saturday; Summer: 9:00 A. M.-5:00 P. M., Monday through Friday.

HOLDINGS: Approximately 184 cubic feet of manuscript and typescript materials, both arranged and indexed. Included are *Records of Synods, Presbyteries, and Congregations of the Associate Presbyterian Church* (1743-1858), ca. 19 cubic feet; *Records of the Presbyteries of the United Presbyterian Church of North America* (1858-1958), ca. 45 cubic feet; *Records of the Congregation of the United Presbyterian Church of North America* (1858-1958), ca. 63 cubic feet; *Records of Congregations of the Presbyterian Church in the U. S. A.* (1787-1959), ca. 25 cubic feet; *Records of the Presbyteries of the Presbyterian Church in the U. S. A.* (1793-1959), ca. 25 cubic feet; *Records of the Synods of the United Presbyterian Church of North America* (1858-1959), ca. 15 cubic feet; *Records of Xenia Theological Seminary* (1855-1930), ca. 2 cubic feet pertaining to this St. Louis institution; and others.

COPY SERVICES: Photocopies. Microfilming can be arranged.

Pottsville

HISTORICAL SOCIETY OF SCHUYLKILL COUNTY

14 North Third Street, Pottsville.

Treasurer: Herrwood E. Hobbs

Hours: 9:30 A. M.-12:00 M., 1:30-4:30 P. M., Tuesday through Saturday.

HOLDINGS: Approximately 54 cubic feet of manuscript and typescript materials, partially arranged and catalogued. Included are *Christopher Loeser Papers* (1815-1860), ca. 18 cubic feet consisting of 6,800 business papers relating to land transactions, legal practice, railroading, and canals; *Edwin Owen Parry Papers* (c. 1807), 50 items of a Schuylkill County judge; *George C. Wynkoop Papers* (c. 1860), 30 items of a Civil War general; *Daniel Yost Collection*, 400 items, miscellaneous items deal with legal matters, land, lumbering, mining, labor, Civil War; and others.

COPY SERVICES: None.

Reading

HISTORICAL SOCIETY OF BERKS COUNTY

904 Center Avenue, Reading.

Director: Mrs. LeRoy Sanders

Hours: 9:00 A. M.-4:00 P. M., Tuesday through Saturday. Make an appointment.

HOLDINGS: Approximately 169 cubic feet of manuscript and type-script materials, only partially arranged and catalogued. Included are *Business Records Collection,* ca. 60 cubic feet: these 18th and 19th C. documents deal largely with the iron industry; *Church Records Collection,* ca. 11 cubic feet includes material from 70 churches; *Personality Collection,* ca. 8 cubic feet of materials pertaining to local personages; *Society Miscellaneous Collection* (1674-present), ca. 16 cubic feet of materials, a good deal of it in German, dealing with the history of Berks County; *Union Canal Records* (c. 1811-c. 1884), ca. 73 cubic feet; and others.

COPY SERVICES: Microfilm and photocopies.

SEE: Mrs. LeRoy Sanders, "Be Your Own Genealogist," *Historical Review of Berks County,* XVIII (April-June, 1953), 75-84.

St. Marys

HISTORICAL SOCIETY OF ST. MARYS AND BENZINGER TOWNSHIP

Municipal Building, St. Marys.

Secretary: Mark C. Lenze

Hours: 2:00-4:00 P. M., Monday through Friday.

HOLDINGS: Approximately 1 cubic foot of manuscript material, mostly arranged, but not catalogued. Included are the *Dr. W. B. Hartman Daybooks* (1873-1889), ca. .50 cubic foot consisting of 5 volumes kept by a St. Marys physician; *Sebastian Wimmer Collection* (1851-1920), ca. .30 cubic foot consisting of 62 pocket daybooks (1851-1912) kept by Sebastian Wimmer, an early settler of St. Marys and a railroad engineer who was prominently connected with the survey and construction of the Mexican National Railroad, and 4 pocket daybooks kept by Dr. Sebastian Wimmer, Jr., (1917-1920), ca. .10 cubic foot of the "Catholic-German Bund organized in Baltimore and Philadelphia in 1842 for settling a colony away from Bigotry"; miscellaneous daybooks, deeds; and others.

COPY SERVICES: Photocopies available.

SEE: *Historical Exhibit of the Historical Society of St. Marys and Benzinger Township,* a pamphlet available from the society.

Scottdale

WESTMORELAND-FAYETTE HISTORICAL SOCIETY

Scottdale.

Secretary-Treasurer: R. W. Westerman

Hours: 2:00-5:00 P. M., Saturday and Sunday, May 15-October 15. Make an appointment. Inquiries should be directed to the Secretary-Treasurer at 303 North Chestnut Street, Scottdale.

HOLDINGS: Approximately 6 cubic feet of manuscript and typescript materials, mostly arranged and catalogued, dealing almost entirely with the local area.

COPY SERVICES: Photocopying can be arranged.

SEE: *Westmoreland-Fayette Historical Society: Catalogue of Museum Exhibits,* a looseleaf catalogue available from the society, which is kept up to date and calendars manuscript holdings.

Scranton
LACKAWANNA HISTORICAL SOCIETY

232 Monroe Avenue, Scranton.

Secretary: Miss Dorothea E. Mattes

Hours: 10:00 A. M.-5:00 P. M., Tuesday through Friday; 10:00 A. M.-12:00 M., Saturday.

HOLDINGS: Approximately 202.5 cubic feet of manuscript and type-script materials partially arranged and indexed. Included are *Delaware and Lackawanna Railroad Papers* (1868-1900), ca. 171 cubic feet of the company's business records; *Col. George W. Scranton Papers* (1845-1860), ca. 2.5 cubic feet of correspondence, mostly business, but containing a few personal items, amassed by a local business leader with interests in iron manufacture, railroads, and coal; *Scranton People Collection,* ca. 15 cubic feet of biographical accounts and letters of prominent Scranton citizens; *Society Miscellaneous Collection,* ca. 6 cubic feet of materials including the minutes of the Susquehanna Company (1791), several David Craft letters, Col. John Franklin items, a Benjamin Franklin autograph, and others; *Genealogical Collection,* ca. 4 cubic feet of typescript family histories.

COPY SERVICES: Photocopying can be arranged.

Selinsgrove
SNYDER COUNTY HISTORICAL SOCIETY

Susquehanna University Library, Selinsgrove.

Curator: William M. Schmure

Hours: By appointment only. Contact Mr. Schmure, 50 Susquehanna Avenue, Selinsgrove.

HOLDINGS: Approximately 3 cubic feet of manuscript material, mostly arranged and catalogued. Included are *Records of Captain C. S. Davis Post No. 148, G.A.R.* (1880-1900), ca. .60 cubic foot consisting of minute books and quartermaster records of this Selinsgrove post; the *Land Warrants Collection,* ca. 2 cubic feet of warrants, most of which are from Selinsgrove and vicinity; a few Civil War letters, genealogical materials; and others.

COPY SERVICES: Photocopying can be arranged.

Shippensburg

SHIPPENSBURG HISTORICAL SOCIETY

Public Library, Shippensburg.

President: Mr. Redmond S. Davis

Hours: By appointment. Address correspondence to Mr. Davis, R. F. D. 1, Shippensburg.

HOLDINGS: A small collection of manuscript, chiefly dealing with organizations and individuals of the locality. Efforts to arrange and catalog the materials are under way.

COPY SERVICES: None.

Smethport

McKEAN COUNTY HISTORICAL SOCIETY

Courthouse, Smethport.

President: C. W. Lillibridge

Hours: 1:00-5:00 P. M., Tuesday and Thursday. It is wise to make an appointment.

HOLDINGS: Approximately .3 cubic foot of manuscript material including letters by Benjamin Franklin, Benjamin Rush, Albert Gallatin, Robert Morris, Samuel Pennypacker, Andrew Stone, Thomas McKean, Henry George, Edwin M. Stanton, and William Howard Taft; miscellaneous deeds; Civil War letters; minute book of the first land company that established an office in McKean County—at Ceres in 1798 (1810) ; and others.

COPY SERVICES: None.

Somerset

MARY S. BIESECKER LIBRARY OF SOMERSET

230 North Rosina Street, Somerset.

Acting Librarian: Mrs. Anna Lebda

Hours: Winter: 10:00 A. M.-9:00 P. M., Monday through Saturday. Summer: 10:00 A. M.-8:00 P. M., Monday, Wednesday, and Friday; 10:00 A. M.-6:00 P. M., Tuesday, Thursday, and Saturday.

HOLDINGS: Approximately 2 cubic feet of typescript material arranged but not catalogued. Included are miscellaneous family histories and the *Somerset County Cemetery File,* ca. 1.5 cubic feet; and others.

COPY SERVICES: None.

Stroudsburg

MONROE COUNTY HISTORICAL SOCIETY

Stroud Mansion, Ninth and Main Streets, Stroudsburg.

Curator: Mrs. Horace G. Walter

Hours: 2:00-4:00 P. M., Tuesday, January through April. Other times by appointment. It is wise, however, at any time to make arrangements well in advance of a visit.

HOLDINGS: Approximately 6 cubic feet of manuscript and typescript materials, neither arranged nor indexed. Holdings include *Bardwell Collection* (1801-1860), ca. .50 cubic foot consisting mostly of business papers of the Depuis or Depuy family, a pioneer family of Monroe County; *Lesh Collection* (1840-1850), ca. .10 cubic foot of personal letters, deeds, and fragmentary financial records pertaining to Pocono tanneries; *Michael Ransburry Collection* (1880-1900), ca. .30 cubic foot of land surveys and other documents mostly pertaining to the building of a branch of the Wilkes-Barre and Eastern Railroad Company; and 2 cubic feet of genealogical material consisting mainly of church and cemetery records, vital statistics abstracted from local newspapers (1840-1900), typed family genealogies including the Colbert materials on the Stroud family, and abstracts from local wills; and others.

COPY SERVICES: None.

See: LeRoy Koehler, "The Monroe County Historical Society, Thirty-Fourth Anniversary, 1921-1955," leaflet printed by the society, 1955.

Swarthmore

FRIENDS HISTORICAL LIBRARY OF SWARTHMORE COLLEGE

Swarthmore.

Director: Dr. Frederick B. Tolles

Hours: Winter: 9:00 A. M.-5:00 P. M., Monday through Friday; 9:00 A. M.-12:00 M., Saturday. Summer: 9:00 A. M.-4:30 P. M., Monday through Friday; closed August.

HOLDINGS: Approximately 2,300 cubic feet of manuscript and typescript materials, almost completely arranged and catalogued, which is divided into three major categories. They are the *Manuscript Collection* (1593-present) which contains mostly collections of papers and journals of Quakers or Quaker-connected people, including Lucretia Mott (1834-1896), Elias Hicks (1779-1830), the Biddle Family (1593-1929), the Truman Family (1819-1885), the Ferris Family (1730-1940), etc.—also in this general classification is a large collection of materials relating to Indian affairs and other social concerns of the Society of Friends; *Friends Archives* (1665-present), the Friends Historical Library is one of the official depositories for records of meetings belonging to the Philadelphia Yearly Meeting of the Religious Society of Friends, and it also has on deposit records of Ohio Yearly

Meeting and 19 of its subordinate meetings, of 9 meetings belonging to Illinois Yearly Meeting, and of Pennsylvania Yearly Meeting of Progressive Friends, and several Quaker organizations such as the Japan Committee of Philadelphia Yearly Meeting, etc.; *Swarthmore College Peace Collection: A Memorial to Jane Addams* (1838-present), the largest of the three major categories that the library's holdings are divided into, the Peace Collection centers around the papers of Jane Addams (1838-1959)—in addition there are papers of other peace leaders, including Devere Allen (1891-1955), Hannah J. Baily (1887-1923), Emily Greene Balch (1893-1948), and Edwin D. and Lucia Ames Mead (1876-1937)—the collection is also the official depository for a number of important active peace organizations including the Fellowship of Reconciliation, Friends Committee on National Legislation, National Service Board for Religious Objectors, Women's International League for Peace and Freedom, and War Resisters League —among the no longer active groups which have deposited their records are Lake Mohonk Conferences on International Arbitration (1895-1917), Committee on Militarism in Education, National Council Against Conscription, National Council for Prevention of War, New York Peace Society, Peace Association of Friends in America, Pennsylvania Committee for Total Disarmament, Pennsylvania Peace Society, and Universal Peace Union.

COPY SERVICES: Photocopies available; microfilming can be arranged.

See: *Friends Historical Library of Swarthmore College,* pamphlet available from the library; and *Guide to the Swarthmore College Peace Collection: A Memorial to Jane Addams* (1947).

Titusville

DRAKE MUSEUM

Pennsylvania Historical and Museum Commission, Drake Well Memorial Park, Titusville.

Curator: A. C. Thompson

Hours: By appointment.

HOLDINGS: A large collection of manuscript and typescript materials dealing principally with the oil industry. The holdings of this depository are being re-organized in the newly expanded Drake Museum. For later information, write to Mr. Thompson.

COPY SERVICES: Photocopies and microfilm are available from the Commission.

Towanda

BRADFORD COUNTY HISTORICAL SOCIETY

Court Street, Towanda.

President: E. Hale Codding

Hours: 3:00-5:00 P. M., Wednesday and Thursday; 7:00-9:00 P. M., Friday. It is, however, wise to make an appointment. Address correspondence to the society at large.

HOLDINGS: Approximately 11.6 cubic feet of manuscript and typescript materials partially arranged, but not catalogued. Included are *Bradford County Cemetery Records* (1813-1933), ca. .40 cubic foot made up of listings of the occupants of 19 old cemeteries; *Count Caesar L. de Chastellux Papers* (1830-1858), ca. .15 cubic foot of legal papers pertaining to Chastellux's land transactions and those of his agents, especially Burton Kingsbury; *Pierre Joseph de Carters Papers* (1817-1866), ca. .25 cubic foot of legal papers pertaining to Bradford County land speculation; *James Le Ray de Chaumont Papers* (1793-1833), ca. .8 cubic foot of business correspondence and legal papers, including 95 letters by Chaumont written to Joseph Kingsberry (1811-1837) and letters from Nicholas Biddle written to Chaumont, Kingsberry, and Henry Welles; *Daybook and Account Books Collection* (1812-1905), ca. 2.5 cubic feet including mercantile records and court dockets; *Amelia Du Pont Papers* (1826-1842), ca. .15 cubic foot consisting of 54 pieces of legal materials pertaining to the New Castle, Delaware, woman's speculation in Bradford County lands; *Piollet Papers* (1812-1907), ca. .15 cubic foot of legal papers and business correspondence of a prominent early family; *J. Andrew Wilt Collection,* ca. 2.5 cubic feet including 21 Civil War period letters of Wilt's and 13 volumes of Civil War pension books kept by Wilt; *Genealogical Materials,* ca. 4.5 cubic feet of records including a file on Bradford County families, and 3″ x 5″ cards kept on Bradford men who served in the Civil War and World War II; miscellaneous materials of interest include road tax transcripts of Burlington Township (1816), Canton Township (1821), and Wysox Township (1817), six David Wilmot letters (1844-1861), a James Buchanan letter; and others.

COPY SERVICES: Photocopying and microfilming can be arranged.

University Park
PENNSYLVANIA STATE UNIVERSITY, PENNSYLVANIA HISTORICAL COLLECTIONS

Fred Lewis Pattee Library, University Park.

Assistant Curator: Wendell McCrae

Hours: 9:00 A. M.-5:00 P. M., Monday through Friday, and by appointment.

HOLDINGS: Approximately 1,500 cubic feet of manuscript and typescript material pertaining mostly to Pennsylvania history, largely arranged, but not indexed. The largest single grouping in the collection is the *George M. Leader Papers,* 300 cubic feet of files of the Pennsylvania governor's office during Leader's administration (1955-1959).

COPY SERVICES: Photocopies and microfilm.

SEE: For a nearly complete listing of the Collections' holdings, Wallace F. Workmaster, "Preliminary Listing of Research Holdings in the Pennsylvania Historical Collections," 1960, a mimeographed listing available from the Collections.

Valley Forge

VALLEY FORGE HISTORICAL SOCIETY

Valley Forge.

Secretary-Treasurer. Mrs. S. J. Wallace

Hours: 9:00 A. M.-5:00 P. M., Monday through Saturday. Make an appointment well in advance because special permission must be obtained before the material can be used.

HOLDINGS: Approximately 1 cubic foot of manuscript materials, neither catalogued nor arranged. Included are 8 orderly books and manuscript letters of various individuals, including George Washington, Timothy Pickering, Baron Von Steuben, Nathaniel Greene, and John Hancock.

COPY SERVICES: None.

Villanova

VILLANOVA UNIVERSITY

Falvy Memorial Library, Villanova.

Librarian: Rev. Louis A. Rongione

Hours: 8:00 A. M.-10:00 P. M., Monday through Friday; 8:30 A. M.-5:00 P. M., Saturday; 2:00-5:00 P. M., Sunday.

HOLDINGS: Approximately 2.25 cubic feet of manuscript and typescript materials, partially arranged and catalogued. Included are the *Alexander M. Thackara Papers* (1866-1897), ca. 1.7 cubic feet of business and personal correspondence of an Annapolis graduate who served in the Navy, the diplomatic corps, and who was associated with his family's business, the Thackara Manufacturing Company of Philadelphia, which made gas fixtures and electroliers; *Joseph McGarrity Collection* (1920-1948), ca. .10 cubic foot of correspondence relating to American sympathy for Irish independence—most of the material dates from the 1920's, but it includes a proclamation of merit for McGarrity from Eamon de Valera (1948).

COPY SERVICES: Photocopies.

Warren

WARREN COUNTY HISTORICAL SOCIETY

210 Fourth Avenue, Warren.

Historian: Mrs. Frances Ramsey

Hours: 9:00 A. M.-5:00 P. M., Thursday, and by appointment. Inquiries should be directed to the society at Box 11, Warren.

HOLDINGS: Approximately 125 cubic feet of manuscript and typescript materials, partially arranged and indexed. Included are *Warren*

County School Records (1830-1960), ca. 14 cubic feet; *Levi Smith Diaries* (1863-1917), ca. 2 cubic feet kept by an oilman who at one time worked in Pithole; *Horn Collection* (1805-1853), ca. 1 cubic foot of records kept by a Warren County father (Daniel) and son (Clinton) who were involved in civic affairs and had lumbering interests—especially interesting are records of a rafting trip to New Orleans in 1806; *Bonner Collection* (1795-1817), ca. 1 cubic foot subdivided into two portions, one dealing with the military career of Capt. James Bonner, and the other containing family papers amassed during the Bonners' residence in York and Warren counties, etc.; *Theodore Chase Collection* (1832-1882), ca. 3 cubic feet, which includes rafting diaries, Civil War letters, business records, and personal correspondence of an individual whose varied careers included lumbering and government service in Harrisburg; *Wheeler-Dusenbury Account Books and Papers* (1830's-present), ca. 10 cubic feet of records dealing with the lumbering industry; *Thomas Clemons Collection* (1825-c. 1890), ca. 9 cubic feet of business and personal papers amassed by a Warren newspaper editor (Warren *Ledger*), lumberman, storekeeper, and educator, including a number of letters written to Clemons during the "Bloody Kansas" period; *Frank Baker Miller Collection* (1765-1960), ca. 12 cubic feet, the bulk of which consists of the papers of the Miller family of Sugar Grove, and traces their history from Brimfield, Mass., in 1765, to Oneida County, N. Y., in 1798, and into Warren County in 1814—also included in the collection are the papers of prominent residents of Warren County, including Robert Falconer, Timothy Davis, David Brown, Robert Cumming, Richard Bishop, John Hamilton, and Gen. Samuel Hays; *John Babcock Collection* (1832-1852), ca. 2 cubic feet includes a journal of a blacksmith shop in Irvine, store accounts from Youngsville, and early church records; *Duntley Letters* (1832-1870), ca. .50 cubic foot of materials of a family living at Corydon, Kinzua, and Randolph, N. Y.; *Wetmore Collection* (1837-1893), ca. 3.50 cubic feet amassed by a family active in local politics; *Ludlow Papers* (1830-1870), ca. 1 cubic foot of business papers (lumbering) and personal letters of the Civil War period; *Irvine-Wynn Papers* (1832-1865), ca. .20 cubic foot of lumbering papers and personal correspondence; *Tunesassa Papers* (1830), ca. .10 cubic foot of records of a Quaker school on an Indian reservation; *Courthouse Collection* (1812-1862), ca. 16 cubic feet; *Ledger Collection* (1793-1849), ca. 10 cubic feet; *Brig. Gen. George A. Cobham Collection* (1863-1864), ca. .25 cubic foot of letters written to his mother and brother; *King Family Papers* (1806-1842), ca. 2 cubic feet dealing with the business interests and family life of a prominent Warren County clan; *Cemetery Records Collection,* ca. 14.5 cubic feet of 3" x 5" cards recording burials in Warren County and nearby cemeteries; *Vital Statistics Collection,* ca. 11 cubic feet of abstracts from family genealogies, census returns, etc., recorded on 3" x 5" cards; and others.

COPY SERVICES: Photocopies.

See: Index to the first eight volumes of *Stepping Stones,* the society's publication.

Washington

WASHINGTON AND JEFFERSON COLLEGE

Memorial Library, Washington.

Librarian: Edwin K. Tolan

Hours: 8:00 A. M.-5:30 P. M., 7:00-10:00 P. M., Monday through Friday; 8:00 A. M.-5:00 P. M., Saturday; 2:00-5:00, 7:00-10:00 P. M., Sunday when school is in session. It is wise, however, to make an appointment.

HOLDINGS: Approximately 135 cubic feet of manuscript and typescript materials, partially catalogued but largely unsorted. Included are *Rev. Henry W. Temple Papers* (1912-1939), ca. 60 cubic feet of a Washington, Pa., college professor turned congressman, which include bill drafts, letters from politicians and constituents, etc.; *Sen. Joseph M. Guffey Papers* (1910-1959), ca. 35 cubic feet of letters, including some of Franklin D. Roosevelt, Harry S. Truman, Theodore Roosevelt, and Woodrow Wilson, and daybooks, most of which deal with the period of the New Deal and later; *Boyd Crumrine Collection,* ca. 10 cubic feet of materials now dispersed through the library collections, including Crumrine's notes for his historical works, original materials he gathered on the Whiskey Rebellion, and a series of letters written by his brother, Bishop Crumrine (1862-1865), which describe the condition of Confederate prisoners in Pennsylvania; *Molly Maguire Collection* (1875-1878), ca. .10 cubic foot of materials concerning the violence which occurred at Connellsville against the Westmoreland and Pennsylvania Gas Company and the Pennsylvania Railroad: these are reports made to Sheriff John Guffey of Westmoreland County and reports to Alan Pinkerton; and others.

COPY SERVICES: Photocopies.

See: Mimeographed guide available from the library.

WASHINGTON COUNTY HISTORICAL SOCIETY

49 East Maiden Street, Washington.

Secretary-Treasurer: Mrs. W. A. H. McIlvaine

Hours: 1:00-5:00 P. M., Monday through Friday.
It is wise, however, to make an appointment.

HOLDINGS: Approximately 1 cubic foot of materials. Included are the *Virginia Counties* [Southwestern Pennsylvania] *Records* (1775-1780), two volumes (restricted) of court records of the West Augusta District and Yohogana County—an additional volume is in the Darlington Library; *Letters of President and Mrs. U. S. Grant to William Wrenshall Smith* (1858-1888), ca. .10 cubic foot of personal letters and invitations; *Vital Statistics Abstracted from the Washington, Pennsylvania Examiner* (1817-1845); and others.

COPY SERVICES: None.

Washington Crossing
THE DAVID LIBRARY OF THE AMERICAN REVOLUTION

Washington Crossing Memorial Building, Washington Crossing State Park, Washington Crossing.

Acting Librarian: William H. Holland

Hours: 11:00 A. M.-5:00 P. M., Monday through Saturday (until 6:00 P. M. under Daylight Saving Time).

HOLDINGS: Consist almost entirely of the *Sol Feinstone Collection* (1750-1798), ca. 1,000 items, arranged and catalogued. The bulk of the materials covers the period December, 1774 through September, 1783, and includes 44 Washington items and miscellaneous papers of Benjamin Franklin, John Hancock, Alexander Hamilton, Thomas Jefferson, James Monroe, John Sullivan, Nathaniel Greene, John and Samuel Adams, Paul Revere, Nathan Hale, and Patrick Henry, etc.

COPY SERVICES: Photocopies available.

Wayne
RADNOR HISTORICAL SOCIETY

Finley House, Beech Tree Lane and Bellevue Avenue, Wayne.

Curator: Mrs. Bertram Wolfson

Hours: By appointment.

HOLDINGS: Approximately .5 cubic foot of manuscript materials neither arranged nor indexed, consisting of a small collection of letters, deeds, and billheads relating to Radnor; interesting individual items are Record of Overseers of Poor of Radnor Township (1765-1810), and the Radnor Township assessment book of 1894.

COPY SERVICES: None.

Waynesburg
GREENE COUNTY HISTORICAL SOCIETY

North Morgan Street, Waynesburg.

Secretary: Mrs. Ralph W. Clark

Hours: 1:00-4:30 P. M., Wednesday through Saturday.

HOLDINGS: Approximately 21.25 cubic feet of manuscript and typescript materials largely arranged, but only partially catalogued. Included are *Cemetery Records Collection*, ca. .25 cubic foot of records of 18th and 19th C. Greene County cemeteries; *Coal Lands Abstract Collection* (1920's-1930's), ca. 8 cubic feet of files which trace titles of Greene County coal lands; *Ledger Collection*, ca. 4.5 cubic feet of business ledgers, justice of the peace dockets, etc., dating from the 19th C. and early 20th C.—although most are Greene County, a few are from

Washington and Fayette counties and from West Virginia; *Military Records Collection,* ca. 2 cubic feet of card files containing information on Greene County soldiers from the Revolution to the present; *A. L. Moredock Collection,* ca. 4.5 cubic feet of genealogical data abstracted from court records in Greene, Fayette, and Washington counties; and others.

COPY SERVICES: Typescripts available.

SEE: "Greene County Historical Society," leaflet printed by the society.

West Chester

CHESTER COUNTY HISTORICAL SOCIETY

225 North High Street, West Chester.

Corresponding Secretary: Miss Dorothy B. Lapp

Hours: 1:00-5:00 P. M., Tuesday through Wednesday; 10:00 A. M.-5:00 P. M., Thursday through Saturday. Closed holidays and August. Address correspondence to the society at large.

HOLDINGS: Approximately 1,555 cubic feet of manuscript and typescript materials, largely arranged and catalogued. Included are an *Autograph Album Collection* (18th and 19th C.), ca. 10 cubic feet; *Chester County Diaries Collection* (18th-20th C.), ca. 50 cubic feet of diaries and memoirs of residents or one-time residents; *Chester County Tavern Papers* (1700-1880), ca. 9 cubic feet of materials which include license applications (1700-1800); *Chester County Tax Assessment Lists* (1699-1850), ca. 48 cubic feet of materials on deposit from the county, which includes records of Delaware County prior to separation in 1789 (1699-1714 holdings scattered, almost complete 1715-1850); *Cipher Books,* (18th and 19th C.), ca. 15 cubic feet; *Records of Directors of the Poor of Chester County* (1790-1930), ca. 24 cubic feet; *Genealogical File,* ca. 260 cubic feet; *Township, Borough, and City Collection* (c. 1682-date), ca. 820 cubic feet of Chester County materials, including business records (ledgers, dockets, etc.), organizational, church, and cemetery records, and municipal records which are arranged and (or) indexed by geographical divisions and then further divided into sub-groups by type of institution; *Postal Collection* (1680's-present), ca. 75 cubic feet of records, correspondence, and memoirs which pertain to the Chester County postal system; *Society Miscellaneous Collection of Personal and Business Letters* (18th and 19th C.), ca. 70 cubic feet; and others.

COPY SERVICES: Photocopying can be arranged.

SEE: Bart Anderson, "The Chester County Historical Society," *Pennsylvania History,* XIX (Apr. 1952), 194-197.

WEST CHESTER STATE COLLEGE

Library, West Chester.

Head Librarian: Joseph K. Hall

Hours: By appointment.

HOLDINGS: A small collection of manuscript materials, neither arranged, nor catalogued. Included are *William Darlington Papers* (1805-1837), consisting of correspondence and professional papers of this West Chester banker and physician; *Anthony Wayne Letters* (1779-1783), 14 letters to and from the military man whose correspondents included Generals Washington, Gates, Irvine, and Greene; *A Set of the Signers of the Declaration of Independence;* interesting miscellanea include 6 letters to Gen. Persifer F. Smith (1836-1855); and others.

COPY SERVICES: None.

Wilkes-Barre

WYOMING HISTORICAL AND GEOLOGICAL SOCIETY

69 South Franklin Street, Wilkes-Barre.

Director: Alan W. Perkins

Hours: 10:00 A. M.-1:00 P. M., 2:00-5:00 P. M., Tuesday through Saturday.

HOLDINGS: Approximately 55 cubic feet of manuscript and typescript materials, partially arranged and catalogued. Included are *Thomas Astly Papers* (1798-1839), ca. .25 cubic feet of legal material pertaining to the Asylum Company, Matthias Hollenback, John Nicholson, and Joseph Kingsberry; *Zebulon Butler Collection* (1770-1789), ca. .15 cubic foot of papers dealing with land transactions in the Wyoming Valley; *Col. Edmund L. Dana Collection* (1861-1868), ca. .30 cubic foot of correspondence and duplicates of official records kept by the colonel of the 143rd Regt. of Pa. Volun.; *Matthias and George Matson Hollenback Papers* (1778-1863), ca. 18.5 cubic feet of papers of local land speculators and businessmen who had interests in the Susquehanna Canal Company, banks, and coal lands; *Hoyt Family Collection* (1799-1865), ca. .45 cubic foot of business papers of this local family and the papers of Col. Henry M. Hoyt of the 52nd Regt. of Pa. Volun. kept during the Civil War; *Samuel and Thomas Meredith Collection* (1771-1842) —Samuel was the first treasurer of the United States and his son Thomas was a lawyer who had extensive land holdings—the collection includes letters from Henry Clay and James Wilson; *Charles Miner Papers* (1814-1858), ca. .70 cubic foot of essays, letters by and from Miner, who was a Luzerne County newspaper editor with a lively interest in politics—this collection contains letters from Henry Clay, James Buchanan, John Marshall, Lewis Cass, etc.; *Timothy Pickering Correspondence* (1787-1823), ca. .10 cubic foot; *Piolett Papers* (1807-1903), ca. 2.25 cubic feet of business papers dealing largely with lumber and land transactions along the Susquehanna in the region of Wilkes-Barre*; *William Plunket Collection* (1772-1776), ca. .05 cubic foot consisting of some 40 items dealing with the first Yankee-Pennamite War; *Hendrick Bradley Wright Collection,* ca. 11 cubic feet of correspondence and political papers of Wright (1808-1881), a historian and an Anti-Masonic figure who became a Democratic congressman; *Genealogy Collection,* ca. 28.1 cubic feet of materials including alphabetical files of Luzerne families, abstracted cemetery records from 77 early Luzerne County cemeteries, and abstracts of Luzerne County wills (1787-1896), will books A-O; miscellaneous holdings include an early copy of a 1779 diary kept by John Franklin, some James Bird material, etc.; and others.

COPY SERVICES: Photocopying can be arranged.

* Related to the Piollett Papers in the Bradford County Historical Society, Towanda.

York

HISTORICAL SOCIETY OF YORK COUNTY

250 East Market Street, York.

Director: Layton Horner

Hours: 9:00 A. M.-5:00 P. M., Tuesday through Saturday. Direct inquiries to Mrs. Arthur Abel, Librarian.

HOLDINGS: Approximately 300 cubic feet of manuscript and typescript material, much of it dispersed in among other materials, partially arranged and catalogued. Included are *John Garrettson Family Genealogy Collection,* ca. 9 cubic feet of genealogical records; *King-Kelley Papers* (1812-1816), ca. .25 cubic foot of personal correspondence, and powers of attorney of a York family which had familial connections in Jamaica; *Samuel S. Lewis Collection* (1924-1942), ca. 1.25 cubic feet of speeches and a few personal papers of a politician prominent in York County affairs; *Local Source Materials Collection* (1749-1940), ca. 30 cubic feet of family, church, and cemetery records of York and Adams counties; *Margaretta Furnace Papers* (1846-1847), ca. .50 cubic foot of letters and account books of the Berks County furnace; *Lewis Miller Books* (1796-1882), ca. .50 cubic foot, the volumes of which contain text and drawings pertaining to York County history, a visit to New York City, and another to Europe; *James W. Shettel Correspondence* (1899-1955), ca. .50 cubic foot of letters to him, mostly from show business personalities—Shettel collected show business memorabilia and his collection is at the society; *Neri W. Shetter Papers* (1926-1929), ca. 1 cubic foot of genealogical correspondence carried on with Pennsylvania families by a genealogist living in Baltimore; *Vital Records Collection* (18th C.-20th C.), ca. 33 cubic feet of materials kept on cards; *York County Land Papers* (1740-1840), ca. 29 cubic feet of land draughts, surveys, and deeds in the society's custodianship from the York County Courthouse; *York County Tax Rolls* (1763-1813), ca. 3.75 cubic feet of material, which has also been abstracted onto file cards; miscellaneous materials include John Durang's "Memoirs," an account of a French-born American professional dancer (c. 1804-1850's), and letters of Thomas Jefferson, James Buchanan, Andrew Jackson, etc.; and others.

COPY SERVICES: Photocopies.

Index

Abbott family, 23
Academy of Natural Sciences of Philadelphia, 30
Account books, 2, 3, 8, 9, 10, 11, 12, 13, 18, 20, 21, 25, 26, 27, 32, 33-34, 38, 40, 42, 44, 46, 51, 53, 54, 55, 56
Adams County manuscript depositories:
  Adams County Historical Society, 13
  Civil War Institute, Gettysburg College, 14
  Lutheran Theological Seminary, 14
  Schmucker Memorial Library, Gettysburg College, 14
  See also Historical Society of York County, 58
Adams, John, 3, 33, 55
Adams, John Quincy, 41
Adams, Samuel, 55
Addams, Jane, 50
Addison, Alexander, *Papers,* 43
Adlum family, 23
Aeronautics, 32
Agriculture, 3, 4, 10, 36, 37
Alaska, 4, 40
Albright family, 22
Aldred, John E., 22-23
Allegheny College, 24
Allegheny County manuscript depositories:
  Carnegie Library of Pittsburgh, 42
  Darlington Memorial Library, 43-44
  Historical Society of Western Pennsylvania, 44
  Pittsburgh Theological Seminary, 45
Allegheny Furnace Records, 1
Allegheny Portage Railroad Books and Papers, 1
Allegheny Valley Railroad, 43
Allen, Devere, 50
Amberson, William, *Collection,* 25
"America First," 8
American Friends Service Committee, Archives of, 17
American Philosophical Society, 30
American Revolution, 1, 3, 11, 17, 36, 42, 52, 57
American Revolution, David Library of the, 55
American Swedish Historical Museum, 31
Anglo-American relations, 33
Annapolis, 52

Anti-Masonry, 58
Armstrong, John, 6
Asbury, Francis, 35
Assessments. *See* Taxes
Astly, Thomas, *Papers,* 57
Asylum Company, 57. *See also* Azilum
Athens Township, 3
Atlantic and Great Western Railroad, 24
Autograph collections, 3, 5, 7, 17, 22, 31, 32, 33, 35, 43, 47, 56
Azilum, 3

Babcock, John, *Collection,* 53
Bache, Richard, *Daybook of,* 32
Baily, Hannah J., 50
Baker, Chester F., *Collection,* 7
Balch, Emily Greene, 50
Baldwin, Henry, Judge, 25
Baltimore, 46, 58
Bank of the United States, First, 36
Bank of the United States, Second, *Papers Relating to the,* 36; 12
Bank of Western Pennsylvania, *Papers,* 24
Banking, 12, 24, 26, 36, 37, 57
Barclay, John, *Papers,* 9
Bardwell Collection, 49
Barker, Charles R., *Collection,* 29
Barony of Nazareth Material, 28
Bartlett, John R., *Papers,* 5
Barton, Benjamin S., 32
Bartram, John, 31
Bassett, Homer Franklin, *Papers,* 30
Bassler, Gottlieb, *Papers,* 15
Bates, Arthur L., *Papers,* 24
Bates, Samuel P., *Papers,* 24
Beaver County manuscript depository:
  Old Economy Village, 2
Beazel Papers, 43
Bell, Edmund Hayes, *Collection,* 20
Benson, Peter, 12
Benzinger Township, Historical Society of St. Marys and, 46
Berks County manuscript depositories:
  Historical Society of Berks County, 45
  Hopewell Village National Historic Park, 11-12
  See also Historical Society of York County, 58; Lebanon Valley College, 3
Bethlehem Public Library, 5
Biddle, Charles, 37
Biddle, Nicholas, 12, 36, 37, 42, 51

Franklin, Benjamin, 3, 5, 32-33, 42, 43, 47, 48, 55; *Papers*, 30, 41
Franklin, John, Col., 3, 47, 58; *Collection*, 3
Franklin and Marshall College, 19
Franklin Institute, 32-33
Free Library of Philadelphia, 33
Frick family, 23
Friedenstal, 28
Friends Committee on National Legislation, 50
Friends, Society of. *See* Quakers

Gallatin, Albert, 5, 48
Garretson, John, *Family Genealogy Collection*, 58
Garvin, William Swan, 26
Garvin and Trunkey Papers, 26
Gas fixtures, 52
Gates, Horatio, Gen., 57
Geddes, James, 22
Geddes Family Papers, 22
"General Registry, Letters of Good Conduct," Bucks County, 1684-85, 10
George, Henry, 48
Georgia, 4
German-American relations, 7
Germantown, 42
Germantown Historical Society, 33-34
Germany, 4, 22
Gettysburg, 5
Gettysburg College, 13, 14, 15
Gettysburg National Military Park, 14
Gettysburg, Soldiers National Cemetery, 5
Gibbs, Oliver Wolcott, *Collection*, 32
Gilbert Collection, 31-32
Girard, Stephen, *Collection*, 34
Girard College, 34
Gloria Dei Church (Old Swedes), Philadelphia, 34
Gnadenthal, 28; *Diary*, 27
Grand Army of the Republic: Captain C. S. Davis Post No. 148, *Records*, 47; W. B. Mays Post No. 220, 13
Grant, U. S., President and Mrs., *Letters to William Wrenshall Smith*, 54
Gratz Autograph Collection, 35
Green, Robert, 23
Green family, 23
Greene, Nathaniel, Gen., 52, 55, 57
Greene County manuscript depositories:
    Greene County Historical Society, 55-56
    See also Historical Society of Western Pennsylvania, 44
Grellet, Stephen, *Papers*, 37
Grey, Asa, 37

Grow, Galusha, 27
Grubb, John, 12
Guffey, John, Sheriff, 54
Guffey, Joseph M., Sen., *Papers*, 54

Haldeman, Samuel Stehman, *Papers*, 30; 37
Hale, Nathan, 55
Hamilton, Alexander, 6, 33, 36, 55; *Monroe-Hamilton Collection*, 5
Hamilton, James, 6
Hamilton, John, 53, *Papers*, 13
Hamilton Library Association, 6
Hancock, John, 3, 52, 55
Harmony Society, 2
Harper, John, *Papers*, 44
Harper's Ferry, 42
Harris, John, 16
Harrisburg, 21, 53
Harrisburg Bridge, 16
Harrison, Ellen Waln, *Collection*, 35-36
Harrison, Thomas Skelton, *Diary*, 38
Hart (s), Samuel, *Papers*, 10
Hart, William Watts, *Papers*, 9
Hartman, W. B., Dr., *Daybrooks*, 46
Hastings, John, Jr., *Papers*, 7
Haverford College, 17
Haynes, S. C., 37
Hays, Samuel P., Gen., 13, 53
Hays, Will, 22
Heckewelder, John, 4
Heidelburg, Pennsylvania, 39
Heilman, Henry Shavely, 3
Helmuth, Justus Christian Henry, *Papers*, 38
Henkel, Paul and Socrates, *Collection*, 38-39
Henry, Patrick, 55
Hicks, Edward, 10
Hicks, Elias, 49
Higgins, Jacob, Col., 2
Higgins, Joseph, *Collection*, 1-2
Higgins Collection, 1-2
Hill, David Jayne, *Papers*, 22
Himes, Charles Francis, *Papers*, 7
Hinke, William John, *Collection*, 20
Historical Society of Pennsylvania, 34-35
Historical Society of the Philadelphia Methodist Conference, 35
Holland, William J., *Papers*, 44
Holland Land Company Papers, 25
Hollenback, George M., 3; *Papers*, 57
Hollenback, Matthias, 3, 57; *Papers*, 57
Hollenback, Mrs. Sarah, 3
Hollenback Papers, 3
Hone, Philip, 18
Hoover, Herbert, 14, 22
Hope Furnace, 23
Hopewell Furnace Records, 11-12

Hopewell Village National Historic Park, 11-12
Hopkinson, Francis, 42
Horn, Clinton, 53
Horn, Daniel, 53
Horn Collection, 53
Hosack, David, 32
Hotel and innkeeping, 1, 12, 28, 56
Howell family, 37
Hoyt, Henry M., Col., 57
Hoyt Family Collection, 57
Hubley, Joseph, *Manuscripts,* 20
Hubley Collection, 8
Huidekoper, Frederick and Alfred, *Letter Books,* 25
Hulings, David W., *Papers,* 7
Huntingdon County manuscript depository:
    Juniata College, 18

Illinois, 4, 40, 49
Independence Hall National Historical Park, 35-36
India, 24
Indian Mission Records of the Moravian Church, 4
Indiana, 4, 40
Indiana County manuscript depository:
    Historical and Genealogical Society of Indiana County, 18
Indians, 4, 17, 28, 30, 37, 40, 42, 49, 53
Inns of Court, London, 36
Insurance, 9, 10, 37, 39
Iowa, 4
Irish independence, 52
Iron manufacture, 1, 2, 6, 7, 9, 11, 12, 16, 21, 23, 26, 44, 47, 58
Irvine, Pennsylvania, 53
Irvine, William, Gen., 57
Irvine, William A., 25
Irvine-Wynn Papers, 53

Jackson, Andrew, 25, 41, 58
Jackson, Sheldon, *Collection,* 40
Jacobs, Barnard, 39
Jacobs, Michael, 14; *Papers,* 39
Jamaica, 58
Japan, 50
Jay, John, 5, 11, 33, 42
Jay's Treaty, 33, 43
Jefferson, Thomas, 33, 37, 42, 54, 58
Jefferson College, Canonsburg, 39
    See also Washington and Jefferson College
Jefferson Literary Society, Mercer County, 26
Jenks, Michael Hutchinson, *Collection,* 10
Jewish records, 39

Jones, John Paul, 36
Jones, Rufus M., 17
Journalism, 8, 10, 22, 26, 53, 57
Juniata College, 18
Juniata County, 17

Kansas, 4, 53
Kearns, Carroll D., Rep., 16
Keating, John, 3
Kelker Collection, 16
Kelley. *See King-Kelley Papers*
Kellog, Josiah, 12
Kennedy, Thomas R., 25
Kentucky, 40
Kiantone Harmonia (utopian society), 43
King, James W., *Records of Official Orders Received,* 38
King Family Papers, 53
King-Kelley Papers, 58
Kingsberry, Joseph, 3, 51, 57
Kingsbury, Burton, 51
Kinzua, 53
Kirkbride, William B., *Collection,* 10
Kuhn, Adam, 22, 32
Kulp Collection, 10

Labor, 13, 43, 45, 54
Lackawanna County manuscript depository:
    Lackawanna County Historical Society, 47
Lafayette, Marquis de, 3; *Collection,* 11
Lafayette College, 11
Lake Mohonk Conference of Friends of the Indians, 17
Lake Mohonk Conferences on International Arbitration, 50
Lancaster County manuscript depositories:
    Franklin and Marshall College, 19
    Historical Society of the Evangelical and Reformed Church, 19-20
    Lancaster County Historical Society, 20-21
    See also Historical Society of Dauphin County, 16
Land dealings, 8, 9, 10, 12, 13, 25, 28, 29, 36, 42, 43, 44, 45, 47, 48, 49, 51, 57, 58
Landis Records, 30
Lane, Harriet, 19
Latin America, 44
Law enforcement, 13
Lawrence County Historical Society, 28
Lawrence County manuscript depository:
    New Castle Free Public Library, 28
Leader, George M., *Papers,* 51

Mercer County manuscript depositories:
Mercer County Historical Society, Inc., 25-26
Thiel College, 15
Merchandising, 3, 9, 16, 20, 23, 26, 29, 36, 37, 51, 53
Meredith, Samuel and Thomas, *Collection*, 57
Methodist church, 24, 35
Mexican National Railroad, 46
Mexican War, 2
Meylert, Secku, 21
Mifflin, Lloyd, family letters, 3
Mifflin, Thomas, Gov., 25
Mifflin County manuscript depository:
Mifflin County Historical Society, Inc., 23
Mikveh Israel, Congregation, 39
Military records, 1, 7, 9, 11, 12, 16, 23, 28, 37, 38, 42, 43, 44, 52, 53, 56, 57
See also American Revolution, Civil War, New York Volunteers, Pennsylvania Volunteers, War of 1812, World War I, World War II
Millcreek school district, 2
Miller, Frank Baker, *Collection*, 53
Miller, Lewis, *Books*, 58
Milling, grain, 3
Miner, Charles, *Papers*, 57
Mining, 26, 41, 45, 47, 55, 57
Minnesota, 4
Mitchell, John K., 32
Moffat, Robert F., *Collection*, 28
Molly Maguire Collection, 54
"Monitor" (Civil War ship), 31
Monroe, James, 55; *Papers*, 41; *Monroe-Hamilton Collection*, 5
Monroe County manuscript depository:
Monroe County Historical Society, 49
Montgomery County manuscript depositories:
Academy of the New Church, 6
Haverford College, 17
Historical Society of Montgomery County, 28-29
Schwenkfelder Library, 29-30
Ursinus College, 8
See also Juniata College, 18
Moore, James II, *Diary*, 22
Moravian Church, 4, 5, 27, 28; Archives of the, 4; Historical Society, 28
Moredock, A. L., *Collection*, 56
Morgan, George, *Letter Books*, 42
Morgenthau, Henry, Jr., 22
Morris, Gouverneur, 3
Morris, Robert, 42, 48
Morton, James St. Clair, Gen., 37
Morton, Samuel George, Dr., 37

Morton Family Papers, 37
Mott, Lucretia, 49
Mount Joy school district, 2
Moyer Brothers Records, 6
Muhlenberg, Henry Melchior, *Papers*, 39
Muhlenberg family, 15
Muncy Historical Society and Museum of History, 27
Muntz, Henry, 15
Murray, Elsie, and Louise Welles, *Collection*, 3
Music, 2, 4

Napoleonic Wars, 9
National Council Against Conscription, 50
National Council for Prevention of War, 50
National Service Board for Religious Objectors, 50
Natural Sciences, Academy of, Philadelphia, 30
Nazareth Hall School, 28
Nazareth Moravian Church, 27
Neagle, John, 37
Netherlands, 22
Neville, John, *Papers*, 42
New Castle Free Public Library, 28
New Church, 6; Academy of the, 6
New Deal, 8, 54
New England, 37
New Jersey, 4, 17, 36
New Market Forge, Lebanon, 16
New Market, Virginia, 39
New Orleans, 53
New York City, 18, 58
New York Peace Society, 50
New York state 4, 33, 37, 39, 43, 53
New York Volunteers: 28th Regiment, 25
Niagara Falls, 29
Nicholls, Griff W., *Collection*, 26
Nicholls, James, 26
Nicholson, John, 57
Nisbet, Charles, 43
Norris, Isaac, 9
North Africa, 9
North American Land Company, 25
North Annville, 3; school district, 2
North Carolina, 27, 39
North Dakota, 4
Northern Liberties Bridge Company, 44
Northampton County manuscript depositories:
Archives of the Moravian Church, 4
Bethlehem Public Library, 5
Easton Public Library, 10
Lafayette College, 11
Lehigh University, 5

Moravian Historical Society, 28
Nazareth Moravian Church, 27
Northampton County Historical and Genealogical Society, 11
Northampton Township, 4
Northumberland County manuscript depository:
See Bucknell University, 22

O'Hara, James, Gen., 44
Ohio, 4, 15, 39, 40, 49
Ohio Company Papers, 43
Oil, 43, 50, 53
Oklahoma, 4
Old Economy Village, 2
Old St. Georges Methodist Church, 35
Old Swedes Church (Gloria Dei), Philadelphia, 34
Oliver, L. Stauffer, *Papers,* 33
Olmstead, George A., 12
Oneida County, New York, 53
Ontario, Canada, 4

Paca, William, 42
Paris Exposition of 1878, 9
Parry, Edwin Owen, *Papers,* 45
Pastorius, Francis Daniel, 34; *Papers,* 41
Patent medicine, 6
Patterson, James, *Business Records Collection,* 20
Peabody, George, *Papers,* 7
Peace Association of Friends in America, 50
Peace movement, 50
Peale, Charles Willson, *Family Papers,* 30
Peale, Rembrandt, 36
Pemberton, Israel, 32
Penn, John, 10, 42
Penn, John, Jr., 10
Penn, William, 3, 17
Penn family, *Papers,* 34
Pennsylvania Canal, 1
Pennsylvania Colonization Society Papers, 23
Pennsylvania Committee for Total Disarmament, 50
Pennsylvania Constitutional Convention, 1837-38, 32
Pennsylvania Folklife Society, *Collection,* 19
Pennsylvania Historical and Museum Commission, 16-17
Pennsylvania, Historical Society of, 34-35
Pennsylvania Peace Society, 50
Pennsylvania Population Company, 13, 25, 43
Pennsylvania Railroad, 54
Pennsylvania Ratification Convention, 36

Pennsylvania, State legislature, 36, 37
Pennsylvania State University, Pennsylvania Historical Collections, 51
Pennsylvania, Supreme Court of, 26
Pennsylvania, University of, 7, 29, 41
Pennsylvania Volunteers (Civil War): 41st Regiment, 1; 51st Regiment, 22-23; 52nd Regiment, 57; 60th Regiment, 3rd Cavalry, 38; 100th Regiment, 28; 128th Regiment, 1; 143rd Regiment, 57
Pennsylvania Water and Power Company, 22
Pennypacker, Samuel, 48
Pensions, Civil War, 8, 28, 51
Perkiomen Valley, 29
Pepper, William, Dr., *Papers,* 42
Pesse, F. J., 3
Philadelphia, 8, 9; buildings, 39
Philadelphia, Bank of, 37
Philadelphia County manuscript depositories:
See Philadelphia city, pp. 30-41
Philadelphia Fire Company Records, 10
Philadelphia Historical Commission, 39
Philadelphia, Library Company of, 36-37
Philadelphia Maritime Museum, 40
Philadelphia Methodist Conference, Historical Society of, 35
Philadelphia Yearly Meeting of the Religious Society of Friends, Department of Records, 32
Physicians, College of, Philadelphia, 31-32
Pickering, Timothy, 52; *Correspondence,* 57
Pierce Family Papers, 26
Pike County manuscript depository:
Pike County Historical Society, 26
Pilmoor, Joseph, Rev., *Journal,* 35
Pinkerton, Alan, 54
Piollet Papers: Towanda, 51; Wilkes-Barre, 57
Pithole, 13, 53
Pitt, William, 43
Pittsburgh, 15, 42; *Common and Select Council Records,* 44
Pittsburgh Theological Seminary, 45
Pittsburgh, University of, 44
Plunket, William, *Collection,* 57
Poinsett, Joel, 37
Portage Iron Works, 2
Potter County manuscript depository:
Potter County Historical Society, 8
Potter County schools, 8
Powel, John Hare, 37
Powel, Samuel, 37
Powel, Samuel (grandson), 37
Powel Family Papers, 37
Presbyterian church, 7, 40-41, 45

United States: Congress, 16, 22, 24, 26, 29, 36, 41, 44, 54, 58; Constitution, 35, 43; 15th Infantry, 23; Navy, 12, 19
Universal Peace Union, 50
University of Pennsylvania, 7, 29, 41
Ursinus College, 8

Valley Forge, 1, 3
Valley Forge Historical Society, 52
Van Dyke, Henry, 41
Vaughan, Samuel, Jr., *Manuscripts*, 32
Venango County manuscript depositories:
    Drake Museum, 50
    Venango County Historical Society, 13
Vergennes, Charles Gravier, 11
Villanova University, 52
Virginia, 10, 38, 39
Virginia Counties Records, Southwestern Pennsylvania, 54

Walker, Robert J., 44
Wallace, Joseph, *Papers*, 16
Walls, John Abbet, *Papers*, 22
Walls, William C., 23
Walls family, 23
Waln, Jesse, 37
Waln, Robert, 37
Waln, Robert, Jr., 37
Waln Family Papers, 37
War Library and Museum of the Military Order of the Loyal Legion of the United States, 38
War of 1812, 13
War Resisters League, 50
Warren County manuscript depository:
    Warren County Historical Society, 52-53
Warren *Ledger*, 53
Washington, George, 3, 11, 31, 33, 39, 43, 52, 55, 57
Washington County manuscript depositories:
    Washington and Jefferson College, 54. *See also* Lutheran Theological Seminary, Philadelphia
    Washington County Historical Society, 54
    See also Greene County Historical Society, 36, 55-56
Washington *Examiner*, 54
Watertown, 42
Wayne, Anthony, Gen., 42; *Letters*, 57
Wayne County manuscript depository:
    Wayne County Historical Society, 18
Webster, Daniel, 12, 14, 37
Weirtheim, A. I., Dr., 39

Weiser, Conrad, 15
Weiss, Jacob, 1
Welfling, Mrs. Mary, 8
Welles, C. F., Jr., 3
Welles, Henry, 3, 51
Welles, Louise, and Elsie Murray, *Collection*, 3
Wesley, John, 35
West Augusta district, 54
West, Benjamin, 42
West Chester State College, 56-57
West Indies, 4; British West Indies, 9
Western Press, Mercer, 26
Westmoreland and Pennsylvania Gas Company, 54
Westmoreland County manuscript depositories:
    Westmoreland-Fayette Historical Society, 46-47
    See also Darlington Memorial Library, 43; Historical Society of Western Pennsylvania, 44; Washton and Jefferson College, 54
West Point, 37
West Virginia, 15, 56
Western Pennsylvania, Historical Society of, 44
Wetmore Collection, 53
Wheeler-Dusenbury Account Books and Papers, 53
Whiskey Rebellion, 54
White, William, Bishop, 41; *Sermons of*, 31
Whitefield, George, 35
Whittier, John G., 17
Wilkes-Barre, 3
Wilkes-Barre and Eastern Railroad Company, 49
Wilkinson, James, 43
Wills, David, 5
Wilmot, David, 51
Wilson, Huntington, *Papers*, 8
Wilson, James, 57
Wilson, Woodrow, 7, 24, 54
Wilt, J. Andrew, *Collection*, 51
Wimmer, Sebastian, *Collection*, 46
Wimmer, Sebastian, Jr., Dr., 46
Wirt, William, 37
Wisconsin, 4
Wistar, Caspar, 32
Witherspoon, John, 41
Women's Christian Temperance Union, 26
Women's International League for Peace and Freedom, 50
Woolman, John, 17
World War I, 14
World War II, 51
Wright, Hendrick Bradley, *Collection*, 57-58

Wright Brothers Aeronautical Engineering Collection, 32
Wynkoop, George C., *Papers,* 45
Wyoming, 3
Wyoming Historical and Geological Society, 57-58
Wyoming Valley, 57
Wysox, 3
Wysox Township, 51

Xenia Theological Seminary, 45

Yankee-Pennamite War, 57
Yeates, Jasper, 36

Yohogana County, 54
York County manuscript depositories:
    Historical Society of York County, 58
    See also Warren County Historical Society, 53
Yost, Daniel, *Collection,* 45
Young Men's Colonization Society of Pennsylvania, 24
Youngsville, 53

Zeamer, Jeremiah, *Genealogical Collection,* 6
Zeisberger, David, 4
Zinzendorf, Nicholas von, Count, 4

A2 05

12-15

H 2 05